ADVANTAGE Grammar 4

MW00611655

Table of Contents

Table of Contents

CREDITS
Concept Development: Kent Publishing Services, Inc.
Written by: Cynthia Dean and Dawn Purney
Editor: Thomas Hatch
Designer/Production: Signature Design Group
Art Director: Tom Cochrane
Project Director: Carolea Williams

Introduction

The **Advantage Grammar** series for grades 3-8 offers instruction and practice in key writing skills, including

- grammar and usage
- capitalization and punctuation
- spelling
- writing good sentences
- writing good paragraphs
- editing your work

Take a look at all the advantages this grammar series offers . . .

Strong Skill Instruction

- The teaching component at the top of each lesson provides the support students need to work through the book independently.

- Plenty of skill practice pages will ensure students master essential skills they need to become competent writers.

- Examples, models, and practice activities use content from across the curriculum so students are learning about social studies, science, and literature as they master writing skills.

Editing Your Work pages provide for mixed practice of skills in a format that supports today's process approach to the teaching of writing.

Take a Test Drive pages provide practice using a test-taking format such as those included in national standardized and proficiency tests.

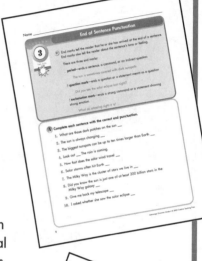

LESSON

1

THE SUN

Understanding Nouns and Verbs

⭐ A **noun** is the name of a person, place, or thing.
   The **sun** is a **star**.

A **common noun** names any one of a group of people, places, or things.
   The **star** twinkled.

A **proper noun** names a specific person, place, or thing.
Proper nouns have capital letters.
   The **Milky Way** is the name of our galaxy.

> **Note:** The sun and the moon are important to us, but their names do not have capital letters. However, the names of other planets do have capital letters.

A **Circle the nouns in each sentence.**

1. The Milky Way is our galaxy.

2. Earth is the third planet.

3. The sun gives light and warmth.

4. Solar wind shoots out from the sun.

5. Solar storms often hit Earth.

6. Sunspots appeared on the sun.

7. Energy from the sun is very strong.

8. The biggest sunspots are larger than Earth.

B **Write a sentence about the sun using two nouns and a verb.**

_____

_____

_____

_____

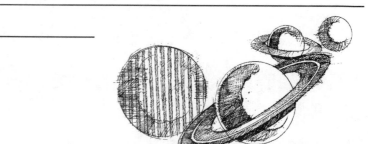

C Complete the chart by listing the common and proper nouns from the box.

stars	Milky Way	planets	Earth	solar wind	sun
energy	Venus	sunspots	solar storms	Mercury	Mars

Common Nouns	Proper Nouns

D Complete each sentence by adding a verb from the box.

is	circled	covered	moves	see	are	look	zooms	burst	were

1. Mercury and Venus _____ bright planets.

2. People thought the sun _____ the Earth.

3. The Earth _____ around the sun.

4. We cannot always _____ solar storms.

5. Solar wind _____ toward the planets.

6. The sun _____ a medium-sized star.

7. Solar flares _____ from the sun's surface.

8. Today the sun was _____ in sunspots.

9. You should not _____ at the sun.

10. The northern lights _____ beautiful.

LESSON

2

THE SUN

Using Adverbs in Writing

 An **adverb** is a word that modifies a verb, an adjective, or another adverb.

The sun shone **brightly**.   **brightly** modifies **shone**
The sun shone **too** brightly.   **too** modifies **brightly**

An adverb answers one of four questions about the word it modifies:

Where?   The comet traveled **near** Earth.
When?   We **often** look to the stars.
In what way?   The solar winds zoomed **quickly** from the sun.
To what amount or length?   I had **just** learned about the solar system.

 A **Circle the adverb in parentheses that best completes each sentence.**

1. The solar flares [suddenly, quietly] exploded on the sun's surface.

2. Solar flares appear [away, near] sunspots.

3. [Soon, nearly] we will learn more about the sun.

4. I [really, rather] believe the greenhouse effect is important to understand.

5. Scientists [very, unexpectedly] discovered sunspots.

6. The sun's rays shone [down, up] on the ground.

7. The buildup of gases will [slowly, barely] smother all living things.

8. He was [very, much] happier to learn about the Milky Way.

B Write a sentence about the sun's effect on Earth. Use an adverb in your sentence.

_____

_____

C Search from left to right and up and down to find 12 adverbs in the word search.

A	X	Q	H	L	P	W	D	F	S	X	B	X
L	Z	U	P	T	B	C	K	A	V	W	I	N
Q	C	I	D	E	M	Y	P	R	B	H	R	O
L	Z	C	N	U	E	C	R	U	D	E	L	Y
M	Z	K	S	G	F	Q	U	N	P	B	L	E
N	S	L	O	W	L	Y	N	E	X	T	Y	T
Y	U	Y	O	T	D	A	B	A	P	X	M	M
C	D	K	N	L	S	C	E	R	E	Q	Y	C
H	D	L	X	Z	W	A	F	J	P	K	G	A
B	E	K	Y	E	X	U	O	F	T	E	N	P
C	N	G	A	F	T	E	R	S	K	W	B	V
M	L	U	C	H	T	H	E	R	E	H	L	S
V	Y	Q	C	E	U	N	P	V	I	C	T	A

D Write each adverb from the word search under its correct category.

Where?	When?	In What Way?

End of Sentence Punctuation

3

THE SUN

⭐ End marks tell the reader that he or she has arrived at the end of a sentence. End marks also tell the reader about the sentence's tone or feeling.

There are three end marks:

. period—ends a sentence, a command, or an indirect question

The sun is sometimes covered with dark sunspots.

? question mark—ends a question or a statement meant as a question

Did you see the solar eclipse last night?

! exclamation mark—ends a strong command or a statement showing strong emotion

What an amazing sight it is!

A **Complete each sentence with the correct end punctuation.**

1. What are those dark patches on the sun ___

2. The sun is always changing ___

3. The biggest sunspots can be up to ten times larger than Earth ___

4. Look out ___ The rain is coming.

5. How fast does the solar wind travel ___

6. Solar storms often hit Earth ___

7. The Milky Way is the cluster of stars we live in ___

8. Did you know the sun is just one of at least 200 billion stars in the Milky Way galaxy ___

9. Give me back my telescope ___

10. I asked whether she saw the solar eclipse ___

  Advantage Grammar Grade 4 © 2005 Creative Teaching Press

Name _____

B Add the correct end marks to the sentences in the following paragraphs.

How does the sun affect Earth The sun gives Earth light and warmth
Energy from the sun causes weather and seasons When the sun's rays
hit the ground, they warm it The warm ground heats the air above it   As the
air heats, it rises and makes wind

The sun also warms the water on Earth   Some of the warm water turns into
a gas and rises into the air   When the gas cools off, it forms clouds   Sometimes
the gases that make up clouds fall back to Earth as rain, snow, hail, or sleet
This is called the Water Cycle

C Periods have other uses. Use a period in most abbreviations.

Initials	S. K. Bryant
Titles	Mr. Jr.
Geographic Locations	St. Wyo.
Time References	A.M. P.M.
Numbers	$7.21 4.2
Business Names	U.P.S. (United Parcel Service) Smith Bros.

Rewrite the abbreviations using periods.

1. 178 Union St _____

2. USA _____

3. 7:45 AM _____

4. Austin, Tex _____

5. 47 Sunset Blvd _____

6. Dr Jones studies solar energy. _____

7. 8:50 PM _____

8. James Jones Sr _____

LESSON

4

THE SUN

Simple and Compound Sentences

⭐ A **simple sentence** has a subject (noun or pronoun) and a predicate (verb or verb phrase).

The sun is always changing. The nine planets in our solar system orbit the sun.
  subject   *predicate*   *subject*   *predicate*

A **sentence fragment** is not a complete sentence—it is missing a subject or a predicate. Here are two sentence fragments.

Solar storms.   Explode on the sun's surface.
   subject   *predicate*

A Underline the subject and circle the predicate of each sentence. Cross out any sentence fragments.

1. Earth is the third planet from the sun.

2. The sun pulls on the planets with a force called gravity.

3. Green plants soak up the sun's energy and turn it into food.

4. Sunspots look like dark.

5. Energy from the sun causes weather and seasons.

Jupiter   Saturn   Uranus   Neptune   Earth   Venus   Mars   Mercury   Pluto

★ A **compound sentence** is made up of two clauses that can each stand alone as a sentence.

Earth would grow warmer and warmer,   and it became too hot for things to live.
subject   predicate   subject   predicate

clause   clause

B Write a checkmark next to each compound sentence. Draw a line between the clauses in the compound sentences.

____ **1.** The nine planets orbit the sun, and Earth is one of these nine planets.

____ **2.** Sunspots look like dark patches on the sun.

____ **3.** Solar storms often hit Earth, but we cannot always see or feel them.

____ **4.** When the sun's rays hit the ground, they warm it.

____ **5.** Sometimes the gases that make up clouds fall back to Earth as rain, snow, hail, or sleet.

____ **6.** The southern lights are called aurora australis.

____ **7.** When meat-eating animals eat the plant-eating animals, the sun's energy is passed on.

____ **8.** The gas cools off, and then it forms clouds.

C Write two compound sentences about the sun.

_____

_____

_____

Name _____

THE SUN

Understanding Paragraphs

⭐ A **paragraph** is a group of sentences that tell about an idea. The first word in the first sentence is generally indented, or placed farther in from the margin.

Many paragraphs follow this structure:

Topic sentence—One sentence tells the main idea. It usually comes first.
Supportive sentences—Sentences gives supporting details about the main idea.
Closing sentence—One sentence retells the main idea.

In the paragraph below, the topic and closing sentences are underlined, and the supportive sentences are circled. The first sentence is also indented.

The sun also warms the water on Earth. Some of the warm water turns into a gas and rises into the air. When the gas cools off, it forms clouds. Sometimes the gases that make up clouds fall back to Earth as rain, snow, hail, or sleet. This is called the Water Cycle.

 A **Read the paragraphs below. Underline the topic and closing sentences, and circle the supportive sentences.**

The sun is a star. It is a huge ball of glowing gases. The sun is one of at least 200 billion stars in the Milky Way galaxy. The Milky Way is the galaxy we live in.

The sun is a medium-sized star, but it is much larger than Earth. The sun is 865,000 miles (1,392,000 km) across. That makes it more than 100 times wider than Earth.

  Advantage Grammar Grade 4 © 2005 Creative Teaching Press

B Rewrite the following paragraph so that the topic sentence comes first, the supportive sentences come next, and the closing sentence comes last. Remember to indent the first word of the first sentence. The topic sentence has been underlined for you.

Green plants soak up the sun's energy and turn it into food. <u>The sun gives energy for living things to grow.</u> When plant-eating animals eat the plants, they receive this energy. The sun is very important to Earth as a living planet. When meat-eating animals eat the plant-eating animals, the energy is passed on again.

_____

_____

_____

_____

_____

_____

C Write your own paragraph about the sun and its effect on Earth. Be sure your paragraph contains a topic sentence, supportive sentences, and a closing sentence.

_____

_____

_____

_____

_____

_____

_____

_____

_____

Name _____

Spelling Common Homophones

⭐ **Homophones** are words that sound alike, but have different spellings and different meanings.

to—is a preposition used to show movement toward something

too—is an adverb meaning "also"

two—is an adjective meaning "second in a series"

A Say each word out loud. Draw lines to connect the homophones in each column.

knows	our	no	pear	
son	wins	Sunday	sundae	
weather	sun	hear	here	
winds	whether	be	bee	
hour	nose	pair	know	

pail	fare	blew	sum	
weight	not	some	raise	
fair	wait	rays	blue	
knot	pale	see	flu	
ate	eight	flew	sea	

B Use four or more homophones in a paragraph about the sun.

_____

_____

_____

_____

C List one or two homophones below each word.

to	fore	they're	sow	by

dear	bare	capitol	scene	one

allowed	clause	groan	reed	rose

steal	tail	weak	hare	bawl

hey	it's	knight	cell	lead

knew	nose	creek	mail	pear

pour	meat	knead	pause	plain

D Circle the homophones in each sentence.

1. The sun rose above the rows of corn.

2. It's amazing how the Earth spins on its axis.

3. I don't know whether the weather will change today.

4. We showed our son how to safely see the sun.

5. I want to travel to the moon too.

6. It was eight before we ate at the Starlight Cafe.

7. You can see our galaxy at the midnight hour.

8. The winds blew so hard I turned blue.

Editing Your Work

7

THE SUN

 Editing your work is an important step in the writing process. Many tests ask you to show what you know about editing.

A **Janice wrote a report about the sun's effect on Earth. Help her revise and edit her work. Read the first few paragraphs and follow the directions.**

   1) The sun affects Earth in many ways. 2) The sun gives Earth light and warmth.

   3) Living things use light and warmth to grow. 4) Green plants soak up the sun's energy, and they turn it into food. 5) When animals eat the plants, they change the sun's energy into energy their bodies can use. 6) When other animals eat the plant-eating animals, this energy is passed on.

   7) Without the son, Earth would not have any life at all. 8) It would be a cold, black rock in space. 9) The sun is very important to Earth.

1. What is the topic sentence of the first paragraph?

   _____

   _____

2. Name four nouns in sentence 2.

   _____

   _____

3. What are the two verbs in sentence 3?

   _____

4. Find the compound sentence in the second paragraph. Draw a line between the clauses, underline both subjects, and circle both predicates.

5. Which sentence uses an incorrect homophone? Write the sentence correctly.

   _____

   _____

   _____

B **Read Janice's account of how the sun creates weather. Then answer the questions to help her revise and edit her work.**

1) Energy from the sun makes whether. 2) When the sun's rays hit the ground, they warm it up. 3) Then warm ground heats the air above it. 4) As the air heats up, it rises quickly. 5) When this warm air meats cold air, it makes wind.

6) The sun also warms the water on Earth. 7) Some of the warm water turns into a gas and rises into the air. 8) The gas cools off. 9) Then it forms clouds. 10) Then the gases fall back to Earth as rain, snow, hail, or sleet. 11) Without the sun, we wouldn't have any weather.

1. Which homophone in sentence 1 is incorrect? Write the correct word here.

_____

2. Name three nouns in sentence 6. Which are proper nouns and which are common nouns?

_____

3. Name the adverb in sentence 4.

_____

4. Sentence 5 has an error. Rewrite the sentence correctly.

_____

5. Rewrite sentences 8-9 as a compound sentence.

_____

_____

_____

Name _____

Take a Test Drive

Fill in the bubble beside the correct answer.

Ryan wrote an essay about the sun. Help him revise and edit his essay. Read the essay and answer the questions that follow.

    1) The sun is a star. 2) It is one of 200 billion stars in the Milky Way. 3) The Milky Way is a group of stars called a galaxy.

    4) The sun is very big. 5) It is 865,000 miles wide. 6) That means the sun is more than 100 times wider than Earth!

    7) The sun a giant ball of burning gas. 8) The middle of the sun is very hot.

9) This is called the core. 10) Its temperature is 27 million degrees Fahrenheit!

    11) Earth is the third planet from the sun. 12) Heat travels from the sun to the planet s. 13) This is called radiation. 14) Our star keeps Earth's temperature just right for us.

1. Which statement is true of sentence 1?
  Ⓐ It is a compound sentence.
  Ⓑ It is a topic sentence.
  Ⓒ It doesn't have a verb.
  Ⓓ It has only one noun.

2. Which word is an adverb?
  Ⓕ star
  Ⓖ middle
  Ⓗ sun
  Ⓙ very

3. How should sentence 7 be changed?
  Ⓐ It needs the verb *is*.
  Ⓑ It needs the verb *were*.
  Ⓒ It needs the verb *be*.
  Ⓓ It needs the verb *am*.

4. Which statement is false about sentence 14?
  Ⓕ It is a simple sentence.
  Ⓖ It is a closing sentence.
  Ⓗ It doesn't have an adverb.
  Ⓙ It has four nouns.

Ryan's class studied the sun. They used a special telescope and recorded what they saw. Read and edit Ryan's report about the sun.

April 2, 2004: 1) We saw five sunspots on the sun today? 2) They looked like dark patches on the sun's surface. 3) The spots are dark because they are cooler than the other parts of the sun. 4) We learned that one of the sunspots is probably larger than Earth.

April 10, 2004: 5) Now there are eight sunspots on the sun. 6) This means the sun is at its solar maximum.

April 11, 2004: 7) Today we saw a solar flare between two sunspots. 8) It burst from the sun's surface in giant loops. 9) It will turn into a solar storm. 10) The sun really is amazing.

5. Which statement is true of sentence 1?
   Ⓐ A period should be used instead of a question mark.
   Ⓑ It is a question.
   Ⓒ It doesn't have a verb.
   Ⓓ The sun is the subject of the sentence.

6. Which word is a noun in sentence 4?
   Ⓕ learned
   Ⓖ of
   Ⓗ larger
   Ⓙ We

7. Which is the correct spelling for a homophone of *ate*?
   Ⓐ eeght
   Ⓑ eight
   Ⓒ eght
   Ⓓ eigt

8. What is the topic sentence of the third paragraph?
   Ⓕ sentence 10
   Ⓖ sentence 8
   Ⓗ sentence 7
   Ⓙ sentence 9

L E S S O N

9

BIOGRAPHIES
OF FAMOUS
AMERICANS

Using Regular and Irregular Verbs

⭐ There are two types of verbs: regular and irregular.

Regular verbs form the past tense by adding *–ed*, or *–d* if the verb ends in e.

> **work**—George Washington **worked** as a planter and farmer.

Irregular verbs do not form the past tense by adding *–ed* or *–d* to the verb. Each irregular verb has its own set of rules to form the past tense.

> **become**—Later, Washington **became** the first General of the Army of the United States.

A **Read each sentence. Decide if the bold verb is regular or irregular. Write R if the verb is regular and I if the verb is irregular.**

_____ 1. **come**—Colin Powell's family **came** to America from Jamaica.

_____ 2. **move**—Powell's family **moved** to the South Bronx.

_____ 3. **send**—In 1962, the Army **sent** Colin Powell to Vietnam.

_____ 4. **learn**—Powell **learned** many lessons during the Vietnam War.

B **Write the past tense form of the verb to complete each sentence.**

1. **find**—Anne Hutchinson _____ there wasn't any religious freedom in the Massachusetts Bay Colony.

2. **name**—William Penn _____ Pennsylvania after his father.

3. **write**—Roger Sherman _____ some of the Declaration of Independence.

4. **become**—Thomas Edison _____ one of America's most important inventors when he invented the incandescent light bulb.

Advantage Grammar Grade 4 © 2005 Creative Teaching Press

B Change each verb from present tense to past or future tense to best complete each sentence.

1. **dream**—Dr. Martin Luther King _____ of a society without racism.

2. **speak**—Harriet Tubman _____ to other slaves and encouraged them to escape from slavery.

3. **ask**—In 2001, President Bush _____ Colin Powell to become his Secretary of State.

4. **declare**—On June 1st, 1812, President James Madison _____ on England.

5. **hope**—Franklin D. Roosevelt _____ that America would come out of the Great Depression.

6. **help**—President Roosevelt's New Deal program _____ many people find new jobs.

7. **finish**—When George Washington Carver was _____ , there were 300 products made from peanuts.

8. **join**—In 1606, Captain John Smith _____ the voyage to the Virginia Colony.

C Write a sentence about a famous American.

_____

_____

_____

_____

Name _____

11

BIOGRAPHIES
OF FAMOUS
AMERICANS

Using Apostrophes

⭐ An **apostrophe** is used to show ownership.

For most **singular nouns**, add an apostrophe plus –s to show ownership.

Annie's books are on the table.

For singular nouns that end in s, if adding an apostrophe plus –s makes the word difficult to say, then just add an apostrophe.

Mr. Burns' poetry made the class laugh.

For **plural nouns** that end in –s or –es, only add an apostrophe.

The sargeants' orders were clear.

For plural nouns that do not end in –s or –es, add an apostrophe plus –s.

Carrie Chapman Catt stood up for women's rights.

A **Circle the correct form to complete each sentence.**

1. John J. Audubon painted many of _____ birds.

   America's   Americas'

2. Rosa Parks was part of the _____ struggle for equality.

   nations'   nation's

3. Thomas _____ many inventions won him fame.

   Edisons's   Edison's

B **Write a sentence or two about Thomas Edison's childhood using words with apostrophes.**

_____

_____

_____

⭐ Apostrophes are also used in contractions. A **contraction** is a phrase that has been shortened by removing one or more letters. The apostrophe is used to show that letters are missing.

are not—aren't

I will—I'll

you are—you're

he would—he'd

did not—didn't

C **Complete the chart with the correct contractions.**

Words	Contraction	Words	Contraction
she will		he will	
will not		I would	
she would		they will	
do not		cannot	
I will		was not	
you will		you will	
I am		were not	

D **Add contractions to best complete the following sentences.**

1. Franklin D. Roosevelt _____ let his physical disability slow him down.

2. Some teachers believed it _____ worth teaching Cesar Chavez to speak English.

3. I _____ believe that the British burned the White House.

4. _____ sure we will learn about William Penn next week.

Name _____

 A **sentence fragment** is a group of words that does not form a complete sentence containing a subject and a verb.

fragments:

Thomas Jefferson and the Declaration of Independence.
Wrote the Declaration of Independence.

better:

Thomas Jefferson wrote the Declaration of Independence.

A **run-on** sentence is a long sentence that's hard to read because it has too many ideas.

a run-on:

Rosa Parks refused to give up her seat on the bus she was riding in Montgomery, Alabama after a long day at work so she was arrested by the police which led to the famous 381-day Montgomery bus boycott.

better:

After a long day at work, Rosa Parks refused to give up her seat on the bus she was riding in Montgomery, Alabama. Her arrest by the police led to the famous 381-day Montgomery bus boycott.

A Draw lines to link the sentence fragments and make complete sentences.

1. Dr. Martin Luther King   invented the lightning rod.

2. Rosa Parks   lead the National American Woman
                                       Suffrage Association.

3. Benjamin Franklin   spoke to Americans about civil rights.

4. Roger Williams   was the 34th president of the United States.

5. Dwight D. Eisenhower   founded the state of Rhode Island.

6. Carrie Chapman Catt   boycotted the public bus service in
                                       Montgomery, Alabama.

B Write a complete sentence about Dr. Martin Luther King.

_____

C **Add a subject or a verb from the box to complete each sentence.**

> James Madison   eat   called   Dr. Martin Luther King, Jr.
> named   received   Colin Powell   became

1. William Penn _____ Pennsylvania after his father.

2. _____ was the fourth president of the United States.

3. Many people _____ Jefferson the "Father of the Constitution."

4. _____ spoke to Americans about civil rights in his
   "I Have a Dream" speech.

5. Dr. Martin Luther King, Jr. _____ the Nobel Peace Prize.

6. Franklin D. Roosevelt _____ president during the Great Depression.

D **Rewrite the following run-ons as two complete sentences.**

1. Benjamin Franklin was a man of many talents who invented bifocal glasses
   and the lightning rod and he also was among those who signed the
   Declaration of Independence, which he also helped to write.

   _____

   _____

   _____

2. Dwight D. Eisenhower after World War II was elected the 34th president of
   the United States, he was also during World War II the Supreme Commander
   of U.S. troops in Europe.

   _____

   _____

   _____

   _____

BIOGRAPHIES OF FAMOUS AMERICANS

LESSON 13

Identifying Paragraph Structure

⭐ The sentences in a paragraph should be connected clearly. Here are four ways to structure a paragraph:

- **cause and effect** – the effect of one thing on another is presented

  Workers like Cesar Chavez used a short-handled hoe to dig up crops. But the worker had to bend low to use the tool. This made the work very painful.

- **statement and example** – the main idea is presented and backed up with examples

  Farm workers are often paid by how fast and how much they can pick. For example, the more grapes they pick, the more money they earn.

- **time sequence** or order – information is presented in the order it happened or should happen

  Cesar Chavez was born in 1927. By 1937, he worked on farms with his family. After eighth grade, Cesar quit school and worked full time.

- **compare and contrast** – two or more ideas are presented and then compared and contrasted

  As a 10-year-old boy, Cesar Chavez worked for 12 to 14 hours a day. However, most American 10-year-olds spend their days in school. How many hours do you spend at school per day?

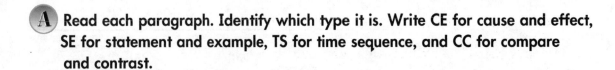

A Read each paragraph. Identify which type it is. Write **CE** for cause and effect, **SE** for statement and example, **TS** for time sequence, and **CC** for compare and contrast.

____ **1.** Because Cesar's family moved all the time, he had no real home to go to at night. Instead, he lived in camps built by the farm owners.

____ **2.** Life was hard for farm workers like the Chavez family. The workers' camps didn't have any running water, any bathrooms, or stoves. Today, most camps are much better, but life is still hard for farm workers.

____ **3.** In February 1968, Cesar began a fast to support the grape strikers. For almost a month, Cesar didn't eat. When he finally ended the fast in March, people called Cesar a hero.

Name _____

> ⭐ Writers use certain words to connect the information in a paragraph. These words are called **transitions**.
>
> **Cause and effect** paragraphs often use these words and phrases:
>
>   as a result   consequently   because   when
>
> **Statement and example** paragraphs use these words and phrases:
>
>   for example   also   for instance
>
> **Time sequence** or order paragraphs use these words and phrases:
>
>   next   then first lastly finally
>
> **Compare and contrast** paragraphs use these words and phrases:
>
>   like   while   however   although

B **Circle the transitions in the following sentences.**

1. Because Cesar Chavez asked people to stop buying grapes, fewer grapes were sold that year.

2. Although their profits shrunk, the grape growers didn't sign Cesar's contracts.

3. First, Cesar tried the long march to Sacramento.

4. As a result, many people learned about the worker's needs.

5. Finally, Cesar united the farm workers.

6. For example, many people stopped buying grapes.

C **Complete the chart by listing each transition above in its correct category.**

Cause and Effect	Statement and Example	Time Sequence	Compare and Contrast

LESSON

14

BIOGRAPHIES
OF FAMOUS
AMERICANS

Spelling Contractions

★ A **contraction** is a word that is shortened by removing one or more letters. An apostrophe is used to show that the letter, or letters, is missing.

A Spell out each contraction completely.

Contraction	Spelled Out Words	Contraction	Spelled Out Words
I'll		don't	
she'll		I'd	
he'll		she'd	
they'll		he'd	
you'll		we'd	
aren't		they'd	
won't		I'm	
can't		you're	
wasn't		who's	
weren't		doesn't	

B Write two or three sentences using contractions.

_____

_____

_____

_____

_____

C **If the contraction is underlined in the paragraph, write the two words that make it up. If two words are underlined, write the contraction they would form.**

Colin Powell <u>didn't</u> _____ have much money growing up. He

<u>was not</u> _____ a good student. He <u>couldn't</u> _____

play many sports well. He didn't _____ know what he wanted to be

when he grew up. But his parents knew that once Colin made up his mind, <u>he'd</u>

_____ do his best.

D **Rewrite the following paragraph using contractions.**

Colin's family was not wealthy. His father, Luther, worked in the stockroom. He would come home tired every evening. His mother, Maud, felt she was not making enough money for the family to survive.

_____

_____

_____

_____

_____

_____

_____

_____

_____

_____

_____

_____

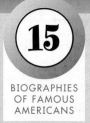

Editing Your Work

15

BIOGRAPHIES
OF FAMOUS
AMERICANS

 Editing your work is an important step in the writing process. Many tests ask you to show what you know about editing.

A **Jaye wrote a biography of Thomas Paine. Help her revise and edit her work. Read the first few paragraphs and follow the directions.**

1) Thomas Paine was born in January 1737 in England. 2) He was born a Quakers son. 3) After a short education, he started to work, at first for his father, later as an officer of the excise, which is a sort of tax collector, and during this time, Thomas Paine was an unsuccesfull man, and was twice fired, or let go, from his post. 4) In 1774, he met Benjamin Franklin in London, who told him to go to America.

5) Paine landed at Philadelphia on November 30, 1774. 6) Starting over as a writer, he published his first work, "African Slavery in America" in the spring of 1775. 7) He said that slavery in America was unjust and inhumane. 8) At this time he also had become co-editor of the Pennsylvania Magazine.

1. Sentence 2 has an error. Write the sentence correctly. _____
_____

2. What is the tense of the first verb in sentence 3? _____

3. Sentence 3 has a spelling error. Write the word correctly. _____

4. Find the run-on sentence. Rewrite the sentence correctly to make it five sentences. _____
_____
_____
_____
_____
_____

5. Name the verb in sentence 5. _____

B **Continue reading Jaye's biography of Thomas Paine. Then answer the questions to help her revise and edit her work.**

1) Since he arrived in America just after the Boston Tea Party, Paine felt the spirit of rebellion grow in the Colonies. 2) In Paine's view, the Colonies had the right to revolt. 3) He'd felt this way because the government taxed them, but would not give them the vote in Parliament.

4) But Paine. 5) He thought the Colonies should not stay dependent on England, they should become a new nation. 6) So, on January 10, 1776, Paines ideas on American independence were spelled out in his pamphlet "Common Sense."

1. Spell out the contraction in sentence 3.

   _____

2. Find the run-on sentence. Rewrite the sentence correctly to make it two sentences.

   _____

   _____

3. Find the sentence fragment. Rewrite the sentence correctly.

   _____

   _____

4. Sentence 6 contains an error. Write the sentence correctly.

   _____

   _____

Name _____

Take a Test Drive

Fill in the bubble beside the correct answer.

Meredith wrote a biography about Cesar Chavez. Help her revise and edit her biography. Read the biography and answer the questions that follow.

1) Cesar Chavez was born in 1927 near Yuma, Arizona. 2) By the time he was 10 years old he worked in the fields. 3) A farm worker. 4) He worked with he's family in the fields of Arizona and California.

5) Cesar's working life was hard. 6) He often 12 to 14 hours a day. 7) Much of this time was spent bent down to work with his hands. 8) Cesar used a tool called a short-handled hoe. 9) He used the hoe to weed the soil. 10) It was "back breaking" work.

1. Which statement is true of sentence 3?
   Ⓐ It is a run-on sentence.
   Ⓑ It is a sentence fragment.
   Ⓒ It is written correctly.
   Ⓓ It is missing a noun.

2. How should sentence 4 be changed?
   Ⓕ Spell the word *field* correctly.
   Ⓖ Rewrite it as two sentences.
   Ⓗ Change nothing—it is correct.
   Ⓙ Change the contraction *he's* to *his*.

3. How is the information in the first paragraph organized?
   Ⓐ time sequence
   Ⓑ statement and example
   Ⓒ cause and effect
   Ⓓ compare and contrast

4. What is missing from sentence 6?
   Ⓕ A subject is missing.   Ⓗ A verb is missing.
   Ⓖ An object is missing.   Ⓙ A noun is missing.

Continue reading Meredith's biography about Cesar Chavez. Help her revise and edit her biography. Read the biography and answer the questions that follow.

1) Cesar's family moved three or four times a year. 2) They traveled to wherever the crops needed picking. 3) Because his family moved all the time, Cesar went to many different schools. 4) But Cesar found his time at school to be very bad. 5) At school, Mexican Americans wer treated badly. 6) Children called these migrant children names like "dirty Mexicans." 7) By year eight, Cesar had had enough. 8) He quit school for good.

9) All this traveling meant that Cesar's family didn't have a house to live in. 10) They slept in cars, tents, and migrant camps. 11) These camps were dirty. 12) They had no running water. 13) They had no bathrooms. 14) They had no stoves. 15) They didn't even have windows to keep the rain out.

5. How is the information in the first paragraph organized?
  Ⓐ compare and contrast
  Ⓑ time sequence
  Ⓒ statement and example
  Ⓓ cause and effect

6. How should sentence 5 be changed?
  Ⓕ Spell the word *wer* correctly as *were*.
  Ⓖ Rewrite it as two sentences.
  Ⓗ Add an apostrophe to the end of *school*.
  Ⓙ Change nothing—it is correct.

7. Which tense is the verb *quit* in sentence 8?
  Ⓐ present
  Ⓑ past
  Ⓒ future
  Ⓓ It doesn't have a tense.

8. Combine sentences 12-14 as a single sentence. Which is the best rewrite?
  Ⓕ They had no running water They had no bathrooms They had no stoves.
  Ⓖ They had no running water, they had no bathrooms, they had no stoves.
  Ⓗ They had no running water, bathrooms, nor stoves.
  Ⓙ They had no running water, They had no bathrooms, They had no stoves.

Name _____

Using Comparatives

⭐ When using adjectives to compare two things, add *–er* to words with one syllable. Double the end consonant if the vowel is short.

large - This box is **larger**.   big - It is **bigger** than the other one.

If a comparing adjective ends with *–y*, change *y* to *i*. Then add *–er*.

heavy - The other bag is **heavier**.

For most adjectives with more than one syllable, add the word *more*.

difficult - It is **more difficult** to carry large, heavy objects.

A **Circle the correct form of the adjective.**

1. A wooden paintbrush is   denser   more dense   than a feather.

2. It weighs more although it is   more small   smaller   in size.

3. It doesn't matter which object is   colorfuler   more colorful.

4. It may not depend on which box looks   more roomy   roomier.

5. After lifting a few things, you may be   abler   more able   to guess accurately.

B **Complete the sentence with the correct form of the adjective given.**

(red)   1. Your face will get _____ when you lift something heavier.

(light)   2. You cannot always tell which object is actually _____ .

(hard)   3. Guessing the weight of some things can be _____ than others.

(stable) 4. Often, dense objects are _____ .

(tiny)   5. The _____ plate holds more.

(rich)   6. Which bag of money would make you _____?

Name _____

⭐ Some adjectives are irregular in their comparative form.

good – better   bad – worse   little – less   far – further

Watch out for common errors.

incorrect: A heavy object is more denser.

correct: A heavy object is denser.

C **Write the correct form above each mistake.**

How dense an object is also determines how it floats in water. How well an

object floats is called buoyancy. Usually a more large object will be less buoyant.

But a heavyer object will also be less buoyant. For example, a ball and a balloon

may not be any biger than each other. But the lighter object, the balloon, will

float gooder than the ball. It will probably float for a more long time, too.

This explains why most women float better than most men. A woman's body

has more fat than a man's. Men's bodies are more muscular. Although fat may

take up more space than muscles, it has littler density. This makes a woman

bouyanter, which means that she floats gooder.

Name _____

Using Superlatives

⭐ When using adjectives to compare more than two things, add *–est* to words with one syllable. Double the end consonant if the vowel is short.

cold - This rock is **the coldest.**   **hot** – Mine is **the hottest** of the three stones.

If a comparing adjective ends with *–y*, change *y* to *i.* Then add *–est.*

icy - The blue glass is **the iciest**.

For most adjectives with more than one syllable, add the word *most.*

heated – Cooling lava is **the most heated** of any rocks.

A **Complete the sentence with the correct form of the adjective given.**

1. Diamonds are the   hardest   most hard   rock of all.

2. Sandstone is one of the   most soft   softest rocks.

3. A topaz is the   yellowest   most yellow   of the birthstones.

4. This opal looks the   most smoky   smokiest.

5. Gems are the   expensiveist   most expensive   rocks.

B **Complete the sentence with the correct form of the adjective given.**

(frosty)   **1.** Spot's nose was the _____of all the rock-hunters' noses.

(sharp)   **2.** Our leader has the _____eyes.

(heavy)   **3.** The least experienced hunter carries the _____equipment.

(delicate)   **4.** Be careful when handling the _____rocks so they don't crumble.

(useful)   **5.** I put the _____guidebook in my backpack.

(wet)   **6.** The _____stones show off their colors best.

38   *Advantage Grammar Grade 4 © 2005 Creative Teaching Press*

Some adjectives are irregular in their superlative form.

good – best   bad – worst   little – least   far – farthest

Watch out for common errors.

incorrect: The most oldest rocks are found in the most deepest areas.

correct: The oldest rocks are found in the deepest areas.

C **Complete each sentence with a word from above or another superlative adjective.**

1. Canyons are among the _____ places to find good rocks.

2. Dinosaur bones are some of the _____ fossils.

3. During the winter is the _____ time to rock hunt.

4. Everyone wants to find the most rocks in the _____ amount of time.

5. Shorelines are some of the _____ places to find rocks with fossils.

D **Write your own sentences using comparative and superlative adjectives.**

_____

_____

_____

_____

_____

_____

LESSON

19

MATTER

Using Parentheses

⭐ Use **parentheses** ( ) to indicate words in your sentence that are not part of the main thought. Punctuation goes outside the parentheses.

All my family (except me) does experiments.

Parentheses can indicate a further explanation.

Odd liquids can be seen around the house in beakers (glass containers used in labs).

A Look at the words in parentheses. Write NMI for "not the main idea" or FE for "further explanation."

_____ 1. Mom sometimes does experiments in the kitchen (I think I drank one last night).

_____ 2. Dad (who is also a scientist) does some experiments in his workshop.

_____ 3. Beakers are usually plastic (or glass).

_____ 4. Anything that fits can go into a beaker (but it's usually used for liquid).

_____ 5. My brother (who's almost 16) does his own experiments.

B Add an ending parenthesis to the sentence.

1. Water (the most common liquid can be used in experiments.

2. You can do many things to liquids (as long as you don't break the container .

3. You can change the temperature of a liquid (by boiling or freezing it .

4. Take an experiment out of the light (or the sunshine to see what it does.

5. Mix something into the liquid to see how it reacts (changes .

6. Or just observe (watch what happens to the liquid over time.

7. You may need to check your experiment every day (or even every hour .

Parentheses can also set apart references, or numbers or letters indicating a list.

My favorite experiment involves refracting light with water *(Handy Science*, p. 49).

Other related ones are in the same book (chapter 3).

Try this first so you will 1) learn about bending light and 2) be ready for the next experiment.

I still need to find (a) a small mirror, (b) a half-gallon carton, and (c) a clean surface.

C. Add parentheses to the sentence.

1. Magic tricks are usually done by 1 distraction of the audience, 2 fancy gadgets, 3 science, or 4 lightning-quick movements.

2. My favorite book explains magic *Sh! Don't Tell* by R. Deisch.

3. I like magic because a it is entertaining and b I like trying to figure out the trick.

4. I want to do magic because A I like to perform, B I enjoy magic, and C I want the fun gadgets!

5. I need to practice a trick called Find the Bunny *Tricky Tricks*, p. 68.

6. Try this magic trick at home it's actually science .

7. Collect the following items: 1 pitcher of water, 2 a penny, and 3 a clear glass.

8. Place the penny under the empty glass on a flat surface .

9. Look through the side not the top of the glass.

10. Pour water slowly into the glass until the penny disappears look through the top to see that the penny is still there .

11. The experiment is called the Disappearing Penny Trick *Bending Light*, p. 174 .

12. To learn more why this trick works, read *Science Through Magic* chapter 8 .

13. Light moves through air differently than it moves through water such as in the ocean.

14. Water refracts or bends the light.

LESSON

20

MATTER

Writing Good Sentences

⭐ **Declarative sentences** state facts.

Different liquids boil at different temperatures.

Interrogative sentences ask questions.

Do we have time to do an experiment with water?

Imperative sentences give commands. The subject (you) is not always stated.

Ask an adult to help with this one.

Exclamatory sentences show strong feelings.

If I can control water, I can control the world!

A Write the kind of sentence it is. Use D for declarative, In for interrogative, Im for imperative, and E for exclamatory.

____ **1.** Did you get an adult's permission?

____ **2.** This experiment is to change the point where water boils (its boiling point).

____ **3.** I love doing experiments!

____ **4.** Collect the following items: a large pot, a measuring cup, a wooden spoon, salt, water, and a thermometer that measures temperatures above 200°F.

____ **5.** To start, the thermometer should be attached to the spoon with the rubber band.

____ **6.** Measure and pour three cups of water into the pot.

____ **7.** Can you adjust the thermometer so that it doesn't touch the bottom of the pan, but is still in the water?

____ **8.** Have your adult put the pot on the stove and turn the burner on high.

____ **9.** Has the water boiled yet?

____ **10.** The water is hot!

Declarative: Most of what we read and say is written like this sentence.

Interrogative: Where is the subject in this sentence?

Imperative: Decide now what kind of sentence this is!

Exclamatory: This sentence is most likely to be shouted out!

B **Rewrite each sentence as the type given.**

(Imperative)   1. You may want to do the experiment in part A with both juice and bottled water.

_____

(Interrogative)   2. Think about what would happen if you continue to boil the water.

_____

(Declarative)   3. Careful - the hot stove can be dangerous!

_____

(Exclamatory)   4. Did the results surprise you?

_____

C **Write an example of each type of sentence.**

Declarative: _____

Interrogative: _____

Imperative: _____

Exclamatory: _____

Name _____

Writing Good Paragraphs

⭐ The **main idea** is the central idea of a paragraph. It is usually stated in the **topic sentence**. The first sentence in a paragraph is usually the topic sentence. But the topic sentence can be anywhere in a paragraph. The rest of the paragraph gives **supporting details** about the main idea.

Read the paragraph looking for the main idea and its supporting details.

> The word *matter* means anything that has mass (weight) and takes up space. Atoms are the smallest pieces of matter. Matter can be anything that is a solid, liquid, or a gas. Even the air around us takes up space although we can move through it. Scientists are still learning about what matter is and what it does.

The main idea is stated in the first sentence. The rest of the paragraph tell more about matter.

A **Read the paragraph looking for the main idea and its supporting details.**

Water easily takes all three states (forms) of matter. The liquid state is what we usually call water. But ice is also water in another state. What happens when you heat water? If it gets hot enough, it becomes steam. Steam is water in the form of gas.

Write TS for the topic sentence and SD for the supporting details.

___ **1.** Water easily takes all three states (forms) of matter.

___ **2.** The liquid state is what we usually call water.

___ **3.** But ice is also water in another state.

___ **4.** What happens when you heat water?

___ **5.** If it gets hot enough, it becomes steam.

___ **6.** Steam is water in the form of gas.

B **Read the paragraph looking for the main idea and supporting details.**

Matter looks and acts differently when it is in a different state. For example, a solid tends to have a definite shape. A liquid does not have a definite shape. It changes shape easily depending on what contains it. Although liquid may change shape, it will generally stay together in one puddle. But gas does not have a shape, nor does it stay together if it is not contained.

Write TS for the topic sentence and SD for the supporting details.

___ **1.** Matter looks and acts differently when it is in a different state.

___ **2.** For example, a solid tends to have a definite shape.

___ **3.** A liquid does not have a definite shape.

___ **4.** It changes shape easily depending on what contains it.

___ **5.** Although liquid may change shape, it will generally stay together in one puddle.

___ **6.** But gas does not have a shape, nor does it stay together if it is not contained.

C **Underline the topic sentence in the paragraph.**

1. Many forms of matter change its state when its temperature changes. For example, most liquids become ice (solids) when it is cold enough. Another event that can change the state of matter is called compression. Compression is when something is squeezed very closely together. A gas can become a liquid if enough pressure is put on it. So there are several ways to change the state of matter.

2. Have you ever put an unopened can or bottle of soda pop in the freezer? If you have, you already know that when a liquid changes to a solid, it gets bigger! This is because of what happens to the atoms. Atoms are the little pieces that form matter. The atoms are always vibrating. The atoms vibrate faster when matter is in the solid state. So as it changes from liquid to solid they need room to move. Therefore they take up more space and the matter gets bigger.

Name _____

Spelling Plurals

⭐ A noun naming more than one is a plural noun.

To make most nouns plural, simply add *−s*.

    one room   two rooms

For words ending in *−ch*, *−x*, or *−s*, add *−es*.

    a box   several boxes

For words ending consonant *-y*, change the *y* to *i*, then add *−es*.

    the city   many cities

A Circle the correct plural spelling for the word given.

1. bus   buss   buses
2. stick   sticks   stickes
3. army   armys   armies
4. match   matchs   matches
5. plate   plates   plats

B Complete the sentence by writing the correct plural spelling for the word given.

(kind) **1.** Some _____ of matter are called conductors.

(object) **2.** Conductors easily carry energy across _____ .

(energy) **3.** Energy that is moved include heat and electrical _____ .

(metal) **4.** Copper and aluminum are two _____ that conduct electricity.

(wire) **5.** Because of this, _____ are made out of these materials.

(switch) **6.** To stop the flow of electricity, wires move apart when you flip _____ .

(mix) **7.** Pure water is not a good conductor, but most water isn't pure. Watery _____ are very good conductors.

(cloud) **8.** Since water is a good conductor, electricity moves through water vapor in _____ .

★ Some nouns have irregular plural forms.

child – children   man – men   person – people   mouse – mice   deer – deer

C Write the plural form of the word.

1. woman _____

2. child _____

3. bus _____

4. story _____

5. deer _____

6. car _____

7. couch _____

8. path _____

D Now find the plural spellings you wrote above and circle them in the puzzle. Be careful not to circle incorrect spellings!

```
X  R  X  C  H  I  L  D  S
W  O  M  A  N  S  R  T  E
O  P  E  Y  O  R  O  S  H
M  A  D  E  E  R  S  B  C
E  T  L  W  Y  L  F  P  U
N  H  N  S  S  U  B  E  O
S  S  R  S  H  C  U  O  C
T  A  P  C  U  M  S  L  E
C  H  I  L  D  R  E  N  S
S  T  O  R  I  E  S  P  R
E  U  P  A  T  H  E  S  H
```

LESSON

23

MATTER

Editing Your Work

★ Editing your work is an important step in the writing process. Many tests ask you to show what you know about editing.

A **Erica wrote an essay about insulators. Help her revise and edit her essay. Read the essay and answer the questions that follow.**

Common Insulators

1) Some matter slows or stops the movement of energy. 2) This way heat or electricity can be stopped. 3) Good insulators include wood, feathers, rubber, plastic, cement, and fiberglass (which is used to insulate homes). 4) Dry air is one of the best insulators of all!

5) Houses need to be insulated for two reasons: (a) to keep the warmth in during the winter and (b) to keep the heat out during the summer. 6) Insulators can do both things – but some are more good than others! 7) Do you know what keeps your house insulated? 8) Ask your parents if you don't know.

1. Which sentences in the first paragraph are supporting details? _____

2. Which sentence in the second paragraph is the topic sentence? _____

3. Which sentence uses parentheses to give further explanation? _____

4. Write the sentence number for an example of each type of sentence.

   Declarative: _____   Interrogative: _____
   Imperative: _____   Exclamatory _____

5. Write the plural spelling of each word.

   energy _____   cement _____

6. Which word in the first paragraph is a superlative? _____

7. Rewrite sentence 6 correctly. _____

   _____

8. Rewrite one sentence in the first paragraph as an interrogative sentence.

   _____

B **Read the rest of Erica's essay and answer the questions.**

1) Another place insulators are used is around wires. 2) Wires are usually made of metal because they are good conductors (they move energy easily.) 3) Wires are used in many places in our homes. 4) Wires bring electricity from pluggs in the wall to lights. 5) They also bring cable wires to our phones or TVs.

6) But electricity can be dangerous to people! 7) If they were just the metal wires, peoples might get hurt touching the wires. 8) So wires are usually covered with some kind of insulator. 9) Plastic seems to be the commonest insulator for wires. 10) If you ever see metal sticking out of a wire, don't touch it (and tell an adult)!

1. What is the mistake in sentence 2? _____
2. Which plural word in sentence 4 is spelled incorrectly? Write the correct plural spelling. _____
3. Which sentence is the topic sentence in the first paragraph _____
4. Which sentence is the topic sentence in the second paragraph? _____
5. Which sentence uses parentheses to give a further explanation? _____
6. Rewrite sentence 9 to correct the mistake.

    _____

7. Write a comparative adjective you would use to compare how long two wires are.

    _____

8. Write a superlative adjective you would use to compare how long three wires are.

    _____

9. Write the plural spelling of each word.
    plastic _____   glass _____
10. Rewrite sentence 6 as an interrogative sentence.

    _____

    _____

Name _____

Fill in the bubble beside the correct answer.

Ryan wrote an essay about what he learned about matter. Help him revise and edit his essay. Read the essay and answer the questions that follow.

Other Matters About Matter

1) In class, we talked about the different states of matter (solid, liquid, gas). 2) Matter can also have many different properties (or features). 3) We learned about some properties including density, size, shape, boiling points, and buoyancy. 4) Other properties involve things like how easily something bends, how well it sticks together, how light passes through it, how well something mixes with another, and how well the matter can burn.

5) What is most interestingest to me is that matter has both physical and chemical properties. 6) Physical properties are things we can measure, like density, temperatures, colors, and shapes. 7) Chemical properties are how one type of matter mixes with another (sometimes they don't mix). 8) Often a chemical change will make the physical properties change too!

1. Which sentence is the topic sentence for the first paragraph?
Ⓐ sentence 1   Ⓒ sentence 3
Ⓑ sentence 2   Ⓓ sentence 4

2. Which sentence has information in parentheses that is not part of the main idea of the sentence?
Ⓕ sentence 1   Ⓗ sentence 7
Ⓖ sentence 2   Ⓙ none of the above

3. Which rewrite of the adjective phrase in sentence 5 could not be correct?
Ⓐ most interesting   Ⓒ more interestinger
Ⓑ more interesting   Ⓓ None, all phrases above could be correct.

4. Which is the correct spelling of the plural for the word *density*?
Ⓕ densitys   Ⓗ densityses
Ⓖ densityes   Ⓙ densities

Ryan wrote a report on energy and matter. Help him revise and edit his report. Read the beginning of the report and answer the questions that follow.

Energy and Matter

1) Matter can have energy. 2) Matter often stores chemical energy. 3) When a chemical change happens (like if it mixes with something else or catches fire), the energy is released. 4) The release of energy may happen as movement, as heat, or as light. 5) Or the matter may even become something different! 6) For example, what happens when a candle burns? 7) The wax gives off heat and light. 8) If it burns long enough, the wax melts to liquid, some becomes smoke, and some becomes invisible gases!

5. Which phrase could not be used to compare two candles?

   Ⓐ hotter   Ⓒ less hot

   Ⓑ brighter   Ⓓ brightest

6. What kind of information is in the parentheses in sentence 3?

   Ⓕ further explanation

   Ⓖ information not directly related to the main idea

   Ⓗ a list

   Ⓙ none of the above

7. Which sentence is the topic sentence?

   Ⓐ sentence 1   Ⓒ sentence 6

   Ⓑ sentence 3   Ⓓ sentence 8

8. Which type of sentence is not in the paragraph?

   Ⓕ Declarative

   Ⓖ Interrogative

   Ⓗ Imperative

   Ⓙ Exclamatory

9. Which noun is not paired with its correct plural spelling?

   Ⓐ candle - candles

   Ⓑ wax - waxs

   Ⓒ gas – gases

   Ⓓ energy - energies

Name _____

25

WESTERN
HEMISPHERE
GEOGRAPHY

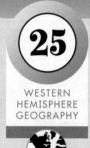

Understanding Pronouns

⭐ Sentences use nouns as subjects and objects. Pronouns can replace nouns in sentences.

NOUNS

Fran took Jim to Mexico.

↖subject ↖object

PRONOUNS

She took him to Mexico.

↖subject ↖object

Pronouns can be singular or plural.

SINGULAR PRONOUNS

He took her to Mexico.

↖subject ↖object

PLURAL PRONOUNS

They took them to Mexico.

↖subject ↖object

Subject Pronouns	
singular	*plural*
I	we
you	you
he she it	they

Object Pronouns	
singular	*plural*
me	us
you	you
him her it	them

A **Circle the subject pronouns. Underline the object pronouns.**

1. Matt loved the mountains around Denver. He explored them often.

2. It was the best birthday ever. Mom and Dad took me on a trip to see the Mayan pyramids in Mexico.

3. José de San Martín liberated the people of Peru. He helped give them independence from Spanish rule.

4. "The eagle is a symbol of the United States," said Ms. Marco. She teaches us about American history.

B **Rewrite these sentences to replace the subject nouns with pronouns.**

   1. Canada stretches across five time zones.

   _____

   2. Aboriginal peoples make up about 4% of the population of Canada.

   _____

   3. Michelle plans to take a trip to the French-speaking province of Quebec.

   _____

C **Rewrite these sentences to replace the object nouns with pronouns.**

   1. Mrs. Marco took the class on a trip to the Grand Canyon.

   _____

   2. We sold chocolate bars to earn money for the trip.

   _____

   3. The class washed cars to earn money.

   _____

D **Write two sentences of your own using subject and object pronouns.**

   _____

   _____

   _____

   _____

   _____

   _____

Name _____

Understanding Prepositional Phrases

 A **preposition** is a word that links two words in a sentence.

Fran and Jim went to Mexico.

preposition   object of the preposition

A prepositional phrase includes the preposition, the object of the preposition, and any other words in between.

Mexico is in the western hemisphere.

preposition   object of the preposition

The family drove through the beautiful countryside.

preposition   object of the preposition

Some Common Prepositions	
to	by
in	across
around	during
through	with
after	like
before	for

A Circle the prepositions in the following prepositional phrases.

1. in South America

2. of the tropical rainforest

3. with 17 million people

4. under pressure to change

Name _____

B Draw a box around the prepositions and circle the objects of the prepositions in each sentence.

1. Costa Rica gained independence from Spain in 1821.

2. The Costa Rican government is bringing back the Jungle Train railroad line for tourists.

3. The rainforests are slowly being cut down for agricultural fields.

4. You must go through the capital city, San Jose to travel anywhere else in Costa Rica.

5. Arenal Volcano in this country has mini-eruptions every hour!

6. Most of the population of Chile live in the fertile heartland.

7. The central regions of Chile have a Mediterranean climate with changeable winters and hot, dry summers.

8. The week before Easter Guatemalans have their biggest festival.

9. If you visit Guatemala, you must go to the Mayan pyramids!

10. The mountains in Guatemala seem to be in eternal spring.

C Underline the two prepositional phrases in each sentence.

1. One-third of the population lives in Santiago, Chile.

2. Columbia has coastlines on the Caribbean and on the Pacific.

3. Most of Columbia is wet and the hot Pacific coastal areas receive 195 inches of rain each year.

4. Heavy snow falls in the Atlantic northeast starting in November.

5. The rock formations in Monument Valley are eroded from red sandstone.

6. Many cities all over the world are named after famous explorers.

Capitalization

LESSON

27

WESTERN
HEMISPHERE
GEOGRAPHY

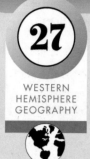

⭐ Use **capital letters** when you write . . .

to begin all types of sentences: Don't move!   Where are you going?

to begin people's names: Benito Juarez

to begin important words in a proper noun:

the Museum of Natural History   Native Americans

to begin a proper adjective: Brazilian people

to begin the names of places: the Great Plains   the Altiplano

Central America   the Canadian Rockies

A **Rewrite each sentence using correct capitalization.**

1. The interior lowlands around hudson's bay make up 80% of canada's land area.

_____

2. The st. lawrence river and great lakes lowlands are the most populated areas of canada.

_____

3. many asians have moved to canada in recent years.

_____

4. kim campbell was canada's first woman premier.

_____

5. the northwest territories cover 1.3 million square miles, or one-third of the country.

_____

B **Choose the sentence that uses capitalization correctly.**

1. Ⓐ Mexico is increasingly considered part of north rather than central America.
   Ⓑ Mexico is increasingly considered part of north rather than Central America.
   Ⓒ Mexico is increasingly considered part of North rather than central America.
   Ⓓ Mexico is increasingly considered part of North rather than Central America.

2. Ⓕ The North American free trade agreement (NAFTA) came into force in 1994.
   Ⓖ The North American Free Trade Agreement (NAFTA) came into force in 1994.
   Ⓗ The north American free trade agreement (NAFTA) came into force in 1994.
   Ⓙ The North American free trade Agreement (nafta) came into force in 1994.

3. Ⓐ Visitors to Mexico are drawn to beach resorts like Acapulco on the pacific.
   Ⓑ visitors to Mexico are drawn to beach resorts like acapulco on the pacific.
   Ⓒ Visitors to Mexico are drawn to beach resorts like Acapulco on the Pacific.
   Ⓓ Visitors to mexico are drawn to beach resorts like Acapulco on the pacific.

4. Ⓕ The Aztec kingdom of Montezuma II was defeated in a war with the Spaniard, Hernán Cortés in 1521.
   Ⓖ the aztec kingdom of Montezuma II was defeated in a war with the spaniard, Hernán Cortés in 1521.
   Ⓗ The aztec kingdom of montezuma II was defeated in a war with the Spaniard, Hernán Cortés in 1521.
   Ⓙ The Aztec Kingdom of Montezuma II was defeated in a War with the Spaniard, Hernán Cortés in 1521.

5. Ⓐ Guatemala and the united kingdom disputed over the new country of Belize.
   Ⓑ Guatemala and the united Kingdom disputed over the new country of belize.
   Ⓒ Guatemala and the United Kingdom disputed over the new country of Belize.
   Ⓓ Guatemala and The United kingdom disputed over the new country of Belize.

6. Ⓕ Once ruled by the British Queen, Belize is now ruled by its own Prime minister.
   Ⓖ Once ruled by the British queen, Belize is now ruled by its own prime minister.
   Ⓗ Once ruled by the British Queen, belize is now ruled by its own Prime Minister.
   Ⓙ Once ruled by the british Queen, belize is now ruled by its own prime Minister.

LESSON

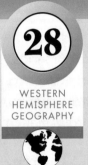

28

WESTERN
HEMISPHERE
GEOGRAPHY

Expanding Sentences

⭐ **Simple sentences** contain one subject and one verb. Often, simple sentences need to be expanded to further explain or clarify the information. Sentences can be expanded by adding adverbs or prepositional phrases to explain how, where, when, why, and what. For example, the following sentence can be expanded to include prepositional phrases that tell where.

The great empire of the Aztecs flourished.

The great empire of the Aztecs flourished in the central valley of Mexico.

A **Expand each sentence by adding information that answers the question in parentheses.**

1. There were many ways pioneers traveled across the country. (How?)

   _____

   _____

2. Rivers are a very valuable resource. (Why?)

   _____

   _____

3. The plantations of the South prospered. (Why?)

   _____

   _____

4. The remaining rainforests are being cut down. (How? Who?)

   _____

   _____

5. The mountains have many minerals. (Where? What?)

_____

_____

6. Between 1860 and 1910, 23 million immigrants crossed the Atlantic and Pacific Oceans. (Why?)

_____

_____

7. Progress is being made to protect the environment. (How?)

_____

_____

8. The geography of California attracts many filmmakers. (Why?)

_____

_____

9. During the 1920s, many African Americans moved to the North. (Why?)

_____

_____

10. The United States has a full range of climate conditions. (What?)

_____

_____

Name _____

LESSON

29

WESTERN
HEMISPHERE
GEOGRAPHY

Spelling Words with qu and kn

 The letters *kn* have the sound of *n* such as in *knee*. The letters *qu* have the sound of *kw* such as in *quit*. In English, the letter *q* is always followed by the letter *u*.

 Use the words in the box to complete the sentences. Use a dictionary for help.

knap	qualified	knack	quartz
knew	quantity	knoll	question

1. She has a _____ for drawing maps that are easy to follow.

2. The _____ of the plateau is at 4,300 feet.

3. North America has large deposits of _____ .

4. The Amazon Basin has a large _____ of insect species.

5. Sean answered the question correctly because he _____ that the Andes mountains were in South America.

6. Jamal _____ to compete at the state geography contest.

7. They found buried artifacts from the Aztec empire underneath the _____ in the hill.

8. Henry asked a _____ about the large oil reserves in Mexico.

B Circle the word that correctly completes the sentence.

1. Canada is (quit   quite   quiet) a large exporter of forest products.

2. Peru is (know   knew   known) as the home of the Inca civilization.

3. No (kites   knights   nights) fought for any part of the
   western hemisphere.

4. Talladega, Alabama is famous for its racetrack and its rock
   (quarry   query   quarrie).

C Write the word from the box that best completes the sentence. Be careful: Not
all words in the box will be used.

> quarrel   known   quiet   quite   knack   quart
> quarters   knock   knapsack   knuckle

1. Where the border actually exists is one thing countries _____ over.

2. The waters are _____ warm in much of the Caribbean.

3. Even if you're alone, the rainforest is never _____ .

4. The Mayans seemed have a _____ for building pyramids!

5. A section of a town called districts, neighborhoods, precincts, or _____ .

6. Chile is _____ for its long coastline and its vineyards.

7. I wish I could try a _____ of the original hot chocolate drink by the Aztec.

8. World-traveling hikers often carry all they need in a _____ .

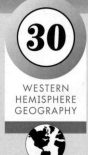

L E S S O N

30

WESTERN
HEMISPHERE
GEOGRAPHY

Supporting Sentences

⭐ The topic sentence in a paragraph is supported by information that explains or clarifies the main idea. There are five main types of supporting information.

Examples: provides specific items or ideas as evidence of support

Details: provides specific descriptions of a person, place, thing, or idea

Facts: provides information that can be proven to support an idea

Reasons: provides an explanation; answers the question Why?

Incidents: relates events to support the main idea

A **Read the paragraph. Underline the topic sentence and circle the supporting information.**

Huge areas of Brazilian rainforest are being destroyed to create farm land and animal pastures. For example, to create enough pasture land for their cattle, ranch owners "slash and burn" the forest. The trees and undergrowth are hacked down and burnt. Then the land is ready for the cattle to graze. However, when ranchers leave this land, the forest takes a long time to grow back. When it does, it becomes thick "secondary jungle" rather than a true rainforest.

B **Below is a topic sentence that begins a paragraph. Complete the paragraph by providing supporting information.**

There are many ways that we can protect the natural resources in our community.

_____

_____

_____

 Advantage Grammar Grade 4 © 2005 Creative Teaching Press

C **Below is a topic sentence that begins a paragraph. Complete the paragraph by providing details or incidents.**

Our field trip to the city dump was more exciting than anyone expected!

_____

_____

_____

D **Below is a topic sentence that begins a paragraph. Complete the paragraph by providing reasons or details.**

After what we saw in our community, we began a kids' club for the environment.

_____

_____

_____

_____

_____

_____

_____

_____

_____

_____

_____

_____

Name _____

 Editing your work is an important step in the writing process. Many tests ask you to show what you know about editing.

 Antony wrote a report about a volcano in Mexico. Help him revise and edit his report. Read the report and answer the questions that follow.

Paracutin

1) Over 60 years ago, a farmer in mexico had an unusual crop pop up in his field – a volcano! 2) He knew something was wrong when he felt earthquakes for two weeks. 3) Soon after the quakes started, he started hearing thunder. 4) But the sky was clear! 5) Then a hole in a knoll on the farm opened up.

6) Things happened quickly from there. 7) They heard thunder again, then noticed that the hole had swelled up. 8) Next smoke and ashes rose out of the hole. 9) The farmer and his wife heard a hissing sound and smelled sulphur. 10) That's when they left the corn for a safer place.

1. Which word should be capitalized in the first paragraph? Why?

   _____

2. What is the pronoun in sentence 2? What does it stand for?

   _____

3. What kind of pronoun is in sentence 3? (Circle one)

   subject pronoun   object pronoun

4. Underline the preposition and circle the object in the following.

   of the hole   for a safer place

5. What are the two prepositional phrases from sentence 5?

   _____

B **Read the rest of Antony's report and answer the questions that follow.**

1) The volcano continued to grow. 2) It rose to 424 meters (over 1,000 feet) high. 3) Not only did the volcano destroy the field, but the lava flows that came next covered two nearby villages. 4) Three people were killed from lightning produced by the volcano. 5) Ash fell so thick on the forests that it killed all the plants. 6) The volcano actually erupted for nine years. 7) It has been quite since that time, and scientists believe that it will stay that way. 8) Tourists still visit the volcano now know as Paracutin.

1. Why are there two capitalized words in sentence 8?

   _____

2. Rewrite sentence 1 and expand it with prepositional phrases.

   _____

3. Write the 2 prepositional phrases from sentence 4.

   _____

4. Underline the preposition and circle the object in the following prepositional phrases.

   on the forests   for nine years   since that time

5. Write the word used incorrectly from sentence 7 and write the correct word.

   _____

6. Write the word used incorrectly from sentence 8 and write the correct word.

   _____

7. What is the object pronoun used in sentence 5 and what noun does it stand for?

   _____

8. Circle the word that best describes how the paragraphs are structured.

   examples   reasons   details

Name _____

Take a Test Drive

Fill in the bubble beside the correct answer.

Haley wrote an essay about a trip. Help her revise and edit her essay. Read the essay and answer the questions that follow.

1) My grandfather took me on a trip to Puerto Rico last year. 2) He had to go on business. 3) Since Grandma couldn't go this time, he took me. 4) But there was one condition: I had to know a little spanish. 5) You see, Puerto Rico is a territory of the united States, but they mostly speak spanish instead of english. 6) I learned to count to one hundred in spanish, but that didn't help me much! 7) Lucky for me, Grandpa Joe knows the language quit well.

1. Which version of sentence 5 has all the correct capitalization?
    Ⓐ Puerto Rico is a territory of the united States, but they mostly speak spanish instead of english.
    Ⓑ Puerto Rico is a territory of the United States, but They mostly speak spanish instead of English.
    Ⓒ Puerto Rico is a territory of the United States, but they mostly speak Spanish instead of English.
    Ⓓ Puerto Rico is a Territory of The United States, but they mostly speak spanish instead of english.

2. Which word from sentence 7 is paired with the correct word that should have been used?
    Ⓕ Grandpa – grandpa   Ⓗ knows – nose
    Ⓖ Joe – joe   Ⓙ quit – quite

3. Which phrase is not a prepositional phrase?
    Ⓐ to go   Ⓒ on business
    Ⓑ on a trip   Ⓓ to Puerto Rico

4. Which word is the object of the preposition from the phrase "to one hundred"?
    Ⓕ to   Ⓗ hundred
    Ⓖ one   Ⓙ none of the above

Read the rest of Haley's essay and answer the questions that follow.

1) The island is in the tropics, so it is beautiful. 2) When we left, it was snowing in St. Paul, but in Puerto Rico it was sunny and hot. 3) Another thing about the weather is that it rained there every day around 2:30. 4) Then it would stop and we could go to the beach again.

5) We went to the capital city of San Juan. 6) It is known for the old fort, el morro. 7) It is over 400 years old and it is still strong. 8) My favorite part of San Juan (besides the beach) is the little frogs. 9) I could hear them everywhere, although I never saw one. 10) They make a sound that says, "coo-KEE" and that is what they are named – coqui. 11) I enjoyed my trip with Grandpa Joe and would definitely go to Puerto Rico again.

5. Which word or words should be capitalized?
Ⓐ Old Fort
Ⓑ Capital City
Ⓒ El Morro
Ⓓ Little Frogs

6. How is the second paragraph structured?
Ⓕ incidents
Ⓖ examples
Ⓗ reasons
Ⓙ details

7. What is the object pronoun from the second paragraph?
Ⓐ they
Ⓑ them
Ⓒ we
Ⓓ I

8. Which word is never used as a preposition?
Ⓕ is
Ⓖ in
Ⓗ besides
Ⓙ around

LESSON

Using Possessive Pronouns

33

BOOKS AND LITERATURE

⭐ A **possessive pronoun** expresses ownership. Notice that they do not use an apostrophe.

This is **my** favorite story!   The book is **hers**.

Use these possessive pronouns to modify a noun: *my, your, his, her, its, our, their*

Don't forget **your** bag! – The word *your* tells more about the noun *bag*.

Use these possessive pronouns alone: *mine, your, his, hers, ours, theirs*

The cool car is *ours*.

A **Circle the correct possessive pronoun.**

1. Many authors write about   them   their   own lives.

2. If you wrote one it would be   yours   your   autobiography.

3. I am thinking about writing   my   mine.

4. My   Mine   favorite autobiography is by Laura Ingalls Wilder.

5. My book is so worn   its   it's   cover is gone.

B **Write the letter of the word that fits best.**

___ 1. Authors sometimes change details about _____ own lives.

___ 2. This may keep the story less confusing and _____ length shorter.

___ 3. Laura combined three of _____ enemies into one: Nellie Oleson.

___ 4. Writers may change the stories, but the stories are still _____ .

___ 5. Your life may be interesting to others – you should write about _____ !

a. hers
b. her
c. their
d. theirs
e. its
f. you
g. yours

C **Use a possessive pronoun to complete the sentence.**

1. Laura Ingalls Wilder wrote about _____ own life.

2. She told a story that was _____ alone!

3. _____ family lived in the Midwest in the 1800s.

4. They wanted to move so they could own _____ own land.

5. Laura's father built the house with the help of _____ neighbor.

6. Can you imagine having to build _____ house?

7. I can't even think of trying to build _____ !

8. Laura also got permission from her husband to write about _____ childhood.

9. Laura tried to write so that it would not sound like her story but _____ .

10. If you read her books, you'll know how much harder their life was than _____ .

11. The prairie seemed to have a life of _____ own.

12. I would never want to trade lives. I like _____ life better!

D **Write at least three sentences about people in your life or things you have. Make sure to use possessive pronouns in your sentences.**

_____

_____

_____

_____

_____

_____

_____

_____

_____

Name _____

Using Demonstrative Pronouns

★ **Demonstrative** pronouns identify or point to nouns.

This is **my** favorite book.   (Refers to a specific book.)

That will be something special!   (Refers to an event or experience.)

A **Underline the demonstrative pronoun in the sentence.**

1. I would like those for lunch please.

2. Will you ever forget this?

3. Yesterday I wanted those.

4. That is my cousin.

5. Is this what I've been waiting here for?

6. He was wearing those.

7. These are the words you need to remember.

8. Such is the way of parents.

9. I want that for my collection.

10. I will put these away later.

B **Read the sentence. Tell what you think the underlined demonstrative pronouns refer to.**

1. I think that <u>this</u> is what I will do with my time. _____

2. I could wear <u>these</u> all day long! _____

3. <u>Such</u> is the life of a baby. _____

4. I don't think you'll get far with <u>that</u>. _____

5. Please don't make me eat <u>those</u>! _____

⭐ Words that are demonstrative pronouns can be used in other ways. Remember that demonstrative pronouns take the place of specific nouns.

That used as a demonstrative pronoun: I want **that**!

That used in other ways: I want **that** car!
                                 I see **that** you want one, too.
                                 I didn't know it was **that** popular.

C **Put a checkmark beside the sentence that uses a demonstrative pronoun. Underline it.**

1. a.___ I think these are mine.

   b.___ I will try on these pants.

2. a.___ She is such a nice person.

   b.___ As such, she is good to know.

3. a.___ You may want this one.

   b.___ This always reminds me of you.

4. a.___ That is a handy tool!

   b.___ My dad thinks that it is the best.

5. a.___ I won't be able to carry those myself.

   b.___ Those girls know how to help.

D **Write your own sentences using demonstrative pronouns.**

1. this

_____

2. that

_____

3. those

_____

4. these

_____

LESSON 35

BOOKS AND LITERATURE

Using Parallel Structure

⭐ Words used in the same way in a sentence should be **parallel**, or in the same form. For example, words in a list should be in the same form.

Not parallel: I like swimming and to hike.

Parallel: I like swimming and hiking.

Parallel: I like to swim and to hike.

Verbs should be in the same tense unless there is a time change.

Not parallel: My sister likes reading; and she also liked sports.

Parallel: My sister likes reading; and she also likes sports.

Parallel: My sister likes reading, but in the past, she liked sports.

A **Circle the letter of the sentence that is parallel.**

1. a) I liked reading the book *Maniac Magee* because it made me laugh.

   b) I like reading the book *Maniac Magee* because it made me laugh.

2. a) In spring, summer, or winter, you never knew where Maniac would show up.

   b) In spring, summer, or in winter, you never knew where Maniac will show up.

3. a) Maniac Magee runs all night, and he kissed a bull.

   b) Maniac Magee ran all night, and he kissed a bull.

4. a) Maniac could outrun dogs and tied the strongest knots.

   b) Maniac could outrun dogs and tie the strongest knots.

5. a) Although *Maniac Magee* is a tall tale, much of it sounds realistic.

   b) Although *Maniac Magee* was a tall tale, much of it sounds realistic.

6. a) Maniac lived with his aunt and uncle, Amanda's family, and with a buffalo.

   b) Maniac lived with his aunt and uncle, with Amanda's family, and with a buffalo.

7. a) Maniac liked running, playing baseball, and to make new friends.

   b) Maniac liked running, playing baseball, and making new friends.

8. a) Everyone called him Maniac, but his real name is Jeffrey Lionel.

   b) Everyone calls him Maniac, but his real name is Jeffrey Lionel.

 Advantage Grammar Grade 4 © 2005 Creative Teaching Press

⭐ There may be more than one way to fix a sentence that is not parallel.

Not parallel: I think good stories should be exciting, realistic, and be unique.

Parallel: I think good stories should be exciting, realistic, and unique.

Parallel: I think good stories should be exciting, be realistic, and be unique.

B **Rewrite the sentence so that it is parallel. Pay special attention to the words in italics.**

1. My favorite author *is* Jerry Spinelli because his characters *were* one-of-a-kind.

   _____

2. The writer Jerry Spinelli usually writes *about* convincing settings, *about* realistic situations, and believable people.

   _____

   _____

3. I like books that *had* surprise endings and also *have* funny scenes.

   _____

4. I like *to write* the endings of stories, but I don't like *writing* the beginnings.

   _____

5. Many writers *start* writing poems and *ended* up writing songs.

   _____

C **Rewrite the sentence so that it is parallel.**

1. After school I will go to the library, pick out a book, and be starting it.

   _____

   _____

L E S S O N

36

BOOKS AND LITERATURE

Titles and Headings

⭐ Titles of long works are put in italics, or underlined. These include the titles of novels, movies, albums, newspapers, magazines, ships, and planes.

My favorite book this year is *Superfudge* by Judy Blume.

Another funny book is *The Celery Stalks at Midnight* by James Howe.

Titles of shorter works are put in quotation marks. These works include titles of songs, chapters, articles, short poems, and short stories.

The poem "Sick" is just one hilarious poem by Shel Silverstein.

Quotation marks go outside commas and periods.

A funny fable is "The Tortoise and the Hare."

 A **Add underlines or quotation marks. (Hint: some sentences may have more than one title in it.)**

1. Try to solve the mysteries when reading Encyclopedia Brown Solves Them All.

2. One chapter that is hard to solve is The Case of the Hair Driers.

3. The Wright brothers named their plane The Flyer.

4. Read about the history of the plane in Aircrafters Magazine.

5. The Very First Plane is the title of the article.

6. People read the forecast in our newspaper, The Westlife Journal.

7. We sang the song You Are My Sunshine together.

8. In the movie Shrek, they redid the song I'm a Believer.

9. The funniest section in the magazine Reader's Digest is called All in a Day's Work.

10. The first chapter in the book Stuart Little is In the Drain.

B **List titles for each.**

1. two of your favorite books:

_____

2. a chapter in a book:

_____

3. two of your favorite songs:

_____

4. the title of a CD:

_____

5. the name of a ship:

_____

6. the name of a newspaper:

_____

7. the names of two magazines:

_____

8. the title of a magazine or newspaper article:

_____

9. the name of your favorite movie:

_____

10. the name of a short story or poem:

_____

C Write a few sentences about your favorite book or CD. Give the title and a short description. Then tell your favorite chapter or song and tell why it is your favorite.

_____

_____

_____

_____

_____

LESSON

37

BOOKS AND LITERATURE

Doubling End Consonants

⭐ Some endings you can add to words have a vowel in them.

-ing   -er   -y   -ed

Often, you must change the root word before adding such an ending An example you know already is forming plurals when the noun ends in consonant -y.

story – stories

If the word ends with a silent *e*, take off the silent *e*. Then add the ending.

ride - rider

If a word ends wth short vowel-consonant, double the consonant.

rid - ridding

A Read the first word. Circle the related word that matches.

1. sit   siting   sitting

2. bite   biter   bitter

3. have   haveing   having

4. fib   fiber   fibber

5. fun   funy   funny

6. give   giver   givver

7. drag   draging   dragging

8. swim   swimer   swimmer

9. tame   taming   tameing

10. race   raced   racced

B Write the root word for the word.

1. batted _____

2. writing _____

3. bigger _____

4. running _____

5. cared _____

6. shining _____

7. dimmer _____

8. baker _____

9. tanned _____

10. raking _____

C Write the letter of the related word that matches.

___ 1. pad   a) loving

___ 2. case   b) framing

___ 3. rat   c) ratty

___ 4. frame d) rated

___ 5. rate   e) sitter

___ 6. sit   f) cased

___ 7. love   g) padding

___ 8. pat   h) patted

LESSON

38

BOOKS AND
LITERATURE

Writing a Paragraph to Compare or Contrast

⭐ To write a compare/contrast paragraph, first think of the things you are comparing, then list all the ways they are alike. Then list their differences.

Next, organize the information. Finally, write a topic sentence to give the main idea of the things you are comparing.

Although they are not the same, the movie *Iron Will* and the book *Stone Fox* are very similar. They should be, considering they are based on the same true story! The main character in the book is named Little Willy, and in the movie, it's Will. Other people's names are different, though. For example, the dog's name is Searchlight in the book, but Gus in the movie. The story takes place in Wyoming in the book and Alaska in the movie. In both, the boy enters a dogsled race to earn money. But in the book, it is because his grandfather is sick and needs money to keep their farm. In the movie, however, he needs the money to go to college as well as to save his mother's farm. One of the biggest differences is that at the end of the book, the dog dies, but he recovers at the end of the movie. Even the title is different – the book is named after the "bad guy" while the movie is named after the hero.

A **Work backwards to see how the compare/contrast paragraph above was written.**

1. Underline the topic sentence.

2. List the similarities and differences below.

_____ \ _____

_____ \ _____

_____ \ _____

_____ \ _____

3. Circle words in the paragraph that signal differences or similarities. What other words might you use?

_____

B **Choose a book you know well. Then think of something else that it has a lot of similarities with it. It can be another book, a movie, or even your own life. Follow the directions to organize a paragraph.**

1. What two things will you compare? _____

2. List the similarities and differences below.

   _____   _____

   _____   _____

   _____   _____

   _____   _____

   _____   _____

3. Write a topic sentence giving a main idea and stating the two things you are comparing.

   _____

   _____

4. Look at the list of similarities and differences. If you have more than five of each, you may want to cross out less important points.

5. Now write your compare/contrast paragraph. Try to use compare and contrast words like you found in number three on the previous page. Remember to add your topic sentence!

   _____

   _____

   _____

   _____

   _____

   _____

   _____

   _____

39

BOOKS AND
LITERATURE

Editing Your Work

 Editing your work is an important step in the writing process. Many tests ask you to show what you know about editing.

A Michael wrote a report comparing two stories by Louis Sachar. Help him revise and edit his report. Read the report and answer the questions that follow.

Two Books by Sachar

1) Although they are not alike at all, Louis Sachar's books Sideways Stories from Wayside School and Holes are both great books. 2) These are two of my favorite books. 3) This author is terrific because all his stories are a little crazy! 4) Besides having parts that aren't realistic, both books also have parts that did seem real. 5) But Holes seemed like it could happen in the real world a lot more than Sideways Stories. 6) In each story, some people have weird names. 7) For example, look at Stanley Yelnats's and Mrs. Gorf's last names. 8) Their names are really backwards!

1. Add what is needed to indicate the titles in the paragraphs.

2. Look at sentences 2 and 3. Tell which sentence uses a demonstrative pronoun. Write the pronoun, and what it stands for.

   _____

   _____

3. List the three possessive pronouns from the paragraph.

   _____

4. Rewrite sentence 4 so that it is parallel.

   _____

   _____

5. Which word in sentence 4 dropped its silent *e* before adding the ending? What is the root word?

   _____

Advantage Grammar Grade 4 © 2005 Creative Teaching Press

B **Read the rest of Michael's report and answer the questions that follow.**

1) There are more differences between Sideways Stories from Wayside School and Holes. 2) For one, Holes is one story. 3) But Sideways Stories was thirty short stories. 4) These were all about a different person. 5) My favorite short story was The Three Erics. 6) On the other hand, Holes has one main character – Stanley. 7) Also Holes took place in three different times. 8) The tone in Sideways Stories was very silly. 9) But, although Holes had lots of funny parts, it's tone was serious. 10) That made it even more interesting. 11) I am glad that I don't have to choose and I can enjoy both stories!

1. Add what is needed to indicate the titles in the paragraphs.

2. Tell which two sentences use demonstrative pronouns. Write the pronoun and what it stands for.

   _____

   _____

3. Write the mistake in sentence 9 and write what the word should be.

   _____

4. Rewrite sentence 11 to make it parallel.

   _____

   _____

5. List the two possessive pronouns.

   _____

6. Which word doubled the last letter before adding another ending? Spell the root word.

   _____

7. List ways the two books are different and similar.

   _____   _____

   _____   _____

   _____   _____

   _____   _____

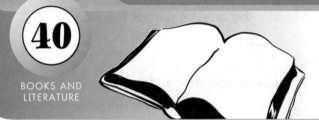

LESSON

40

BOOKS AND LITERATURE

Take a Test Drive

Fill in the bubble beside the correct answer.

Amber wrote a report comparing a favorite book with its movie. Help her revise and edit her report. Read the report and answer the questions that follow.

HOLES

1) When I saw that there was a movie version of my favorite book, I was so excited! 2) The book <u>Holes</u> and the movie "Holes" have very few differences between them. 3) That is probably because the same person wrote both! 4) The differences that are there did not take away from the story. 5) One thing that was not the same in the movie was that Stanley was not fat, but skinny! 6) They explained on the DVD that they had to do that because the actor who played the role had to be able to do all his digging scenes. 7) One thing the movie has but the book didn't is that a camper established the kid's order of importance.

1. How would you correct sentence 2?
   Ⓐ Change the word *them* to *their* to make a possessive pronoun.
   Ⓑ Take away the underline in the book title Holes and add quotation marks.
   Ⓒ Take away the quotation marks in the movie title "Holes" and add an underline.
   Ⓓ Change the word *have* to *has* to make it parallel.

2. Which phrase contains *that* as a demonstrative pronoun?
   Ⓕ When I saw that   Ⓗ One thing that was not the same
   Ⓖ The differences that are there   Ⓙ they had to do that

3. Which sentence is the topic sentence for this compare/contrast paragraph?
   Ⓐ sentence 1   Ⓒ sentence 5
   Ⓑ sentence 2   Ⓓ sentence 7

4. Which is not a way to make the beginning of sentence 7 parallel?
   Ⓕ One thing the movie has but the book doesn't
   Ⓖ One thing the movie had but the book didn't
   Ⓗ One thing the movie had but the book doesn't
   Ⓙ None of the above

    Advantage Grammar Grade 4 © 2005 Creative Teaching Press

Continue revising and editing Amber's report.

1) The other differences were things in the book, but not the movie. 2) The book showed more about Stanley's life before Camp Green Lake. 3) It also showed his letters to and from his mom. 4) Plus the book has Zero's version of the song. 5) We also get to see him a little more with his mom at the end. 6) Such small details as these didn't hurt the movie at all, although I'm glad I read the book too.

5. Which version of sentence 1 is parallel?
   Ⓐ The other differences were things in the book, but not the movie.
   Ⓑ The other differences were things in the book, but not in the movie.
   Ⓒ The other differences are things in the book, but not the movie.
   Ⓓ The other differences were things of the book, but not the movie.

6. Which word needs to double its last letter when adding the *-ing* ending?
   Ⓕ show   Ⓗ get
   Ⓖ have   Ⓙ hurt

7. Which word is a possessive pronoun?
   Ⓐ Stanley's
   Ⓑ his
   Ⓒ Zero's
   Ⓓ I'm

8. Which word in sentence 6 is used as a demonstrative pronoun?
   Ⓕ these
   Ⓖ Such
   Ⓗ the
   Ⓙ I

9. Which words need to be in quotation marks?
   Ⓐ Stanley
   Ⓑ Camp Green Lake
   Ⓒ Zero's version of the song
   Ⓓ none of the above

LESSON

41

JUST FOR FUN

ADMIT ONE

Using Adjectives in Writing

★ Adjectives describe nouns.

friendly   purple   four   that   silky   American   new

When two adjectives come together before a noun, place a comma between them if the word *and* makes sense between them.

beautiful, tasty meal   ten black cards

For more than two adjectives, use commas to separate them. You may need to add the word *and* between them, especially if the adjective ends the sentence.

Look at the giant, red, clown shoe.

The horse was tall, brown, and furious.

A Add the adjectives and the correct punctuation, if needed.

1. (delicious) Her cookies taste _____ .

2. (old, log) We stayed in an _____ cabin.

3. (some, pink) She had _____ flowers in a vase.

4. (little, white) We rode in a _____ canoe.

5. (long, rolling, fast) The river was _____ .

6. (peaceful) It was still a _____ ride.

7. (steady, even) We paddled with _____ strokes.

8. (old, worn) The van that picked us up at the end was _____.

9. (tired, sore, happy) We all felt _____ after our trip.

10. (cheerful, young, Asian) Our guide had been a _____ woman.

11. (crustless, ham) She had packed _____ sandwiches for us.

12. (big, white, cowboy) She looked silly in a _____ hat.

⭐ Add a prefix or another word to an adjective to describe its opposite.

unfriendly   dislike   less patient   the least happy

B **Write a sentence using an opposite description.**

1. (not interested)

_____

_____

2. (not surprised)

_____

_____

3. (not lonely)

_____

_____

4. (not like)

_____

_____

C **Write your own sentences describing something. You might describe a favorite sport, person, book, or something else that interests you.**

_____

_____

_____

_____

Name _____

Using Prepositional Phrases

⭐ A prepositional phrase is used to show how things are related.

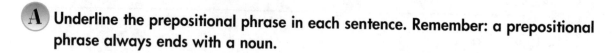

on the carpet   under the carpet   near the carpet   by the carpet

Prepositional phrases also give time and place information, or tell a condition in which something happens.

until class begins   except for me   without mustard

A **Underline the prepositional phrase in each sentence. Remember: a prepositional phrase always ends with a noun.**

1. He grabbed the ball from the floor.

2. He passed the ball to another player.

3. He ran down the court.

4. He stayed in front of the basketball hoop.

5. The team thought that winning was of the greatest importance.

6. His teammate passed the ball back to him.

7. He waited until the best moment.

8. He shot the ball around an opponent.

9. The ball went through the hoop.

10. It was his best game according to his fans.

11. He said he couldn't have done it without his teammates.

12. He was a good sport throughout the season.

Advantage Grammar Grade 4 © 2005 Creative Teaching Press

⭐ **Prepositions**

about, above, across, after, around, at, before, behind, below, beside, between, by, during, except, for, from, in, into, near, of, over, through, to, toward, under, until, with, without, because of, instead of, out of

Many words that are prepositions can act as different parts of speech as well.

prepositional phrase: I ran to the store.

not a prepositional phrase: I had to hurry.

Remember: A preposition starts each prepositional phrase and a noun ends it.

B **Put a checkmark beside each sentence with a prepositional phrase. Underline the phrase – if there is one!**

____ 1. The marble fell through the crack.

____ 2. The phone call finally went through.

____ 3. I was happy because of his kind words.

____ 4. I was happy because they came.

____ 5. I've heard that before!

____ 6. We'll see if he's here before leaving.

____ 7. At noon, we will break.

____ 8. We may eat at the park.

____ 9. Instead of waiting, we'll call him.

____ 10. We'll have juice instead of milk.

C **Write your own prepositional phrase to answer the question and complete each sentence.**

1. The famous athlete will come here (when?) _____ .

2. The famous athlete will come here (how?) _____ .

3. I carried the bag (with what?) _____ .

4. I carried the bag (where?) _____ .

Name _____

Complex Sentences

⭐ A clause has both a subject and a predicate.

If a clause can stand alone, it is an independent clause.

(I) started piano lessons.   (Music) is great.

If a clause cannot stand alone, it is a dependent clause.

When (I) was nine.   Because (she) wanted me to.

A complex sentence has both an independent and a dependent clause.

Ever since (I) was little, (I) wanted to learn.

A Put a checkmark beside each complex sentence. Circle both subjects and underline both predicates in each.

____ 1. I can play the piano.

____ 2. As soon as I could reach the pedals, I started taking lessons.

____ 3. My teacher was nice, but strict.

____ 4. I thought that it would be easier.

____ 5. I wanted to play more interesting songs.

____ 6. Sometimes I didn't want to practice.

____ 7. But I stuck with it, so my music improved.

____ 8. Sometimes I wonder why I keep learning.

____ 9. Yesterday I played for my best friend.

____ 10. He sang along and that made me very proud.

____ 11. Even though it can be work, it is worth it!

____ 12. Do you play an instrument?

Advantage Grammar Grade 4 © 2005 Creative Teaching Press

B Combine one independent clause and one dependent to create a complex sentence. Add any conjunctions or commas and remember to use capital letters and end punctuation.

<u>Independent Clauses</u>

my sister wanted to learn
she often acted
she was only a white belt
my sister worked hard
someday she'll be a black belt

<u>Dependent Clauses</u>

before she was my age
if she sticks with it
when she started classes
so that she could become a brown belt
like she was a karate black belt

_____

_____

_____

_____

_____

_____

_____

_____

C Write three of your own complex sentences.

_____

_____

_____

_____

_____

_____

Name _____

Using Commas in Direct Quotes

⭐ Quotation marks surround the exact words someone said. End punctuation goes inside the quotation marks.

"Who here can tell a good joke?" asked Megan, the club president.

Use a comma instead of a period in a quote if there are more words in the sentence.

"I could if I knew what to tell it," said Jon.

Megan said, "It sounds like you're ready for a joke-off, Jon."

A **Add quotation marks to the jokes.**

1. Jon said, What has 18 legs and catches flies?

   That sounds like a baseball team, said Megan.

2. What do you do when 19 guys are running at you? asked Megan.

   Run faster? said Jon.

   Megan said, No, you throw the football!

3. Why was Cinderella thrown off the basketball team? asked Jon.

   Megan said, Because her glass slippers kept breaking?

   Because she ran away from the ball, said Jon.

4. Why did the golfer bring an extra pair of pants? asked Megan.

   Jon said, You got me there – why?

   In case he got a hole in one, said Megan.

B Add punctuation to the jokes.

1. Why didn't the nose make the volleyball team asked Jon

   I don't know said Megan

   Jon said, Because it didn't get picked

C Add punctuation to each joke. Underline letters that should be capitalized.

1. Megan asked why did the coach go to the bank

   perhaps he wanted to get his quarterback said Jon

2. why can't you take a chicken to go fishing asked Megan

   because the clucking will scare the fish away said Jon

   well, yes, and the chicken will eat all the bait said Megan

D Write three more jokes for Megan and Jon using quotes.

_____

_____

_____

_____

_____

_____

_____

_____

_____

Name _____

Spelling Compound Words

★ Most compound words are two words combined to make another word.

wallpaper   download   keyboard

 Combine words in the box to spell as many compound words as possible.

| book   fly   day   man   note   box   fast   some   sleep   in   butter |
| every   no   day   where   cave   night   mid   break   over |

_____

_____

_____

_____

_____

_____

_____

_____

_____

_____

_____

_____

_____

Advantage Grammar Grade 4 © 2005 Creative Teaching Press

⭐ **Spelling Compound Words**

Some compound words use a hyphen to connect the words.

e-mail   part-time   mother-in-law

Open compound words have a space between the two words, yet act as one word.

mouse pad   post office   chat room

B **Write the letter of the compound word that best completes the sentence.**

___ **1.** Remember to _____ your hair before going outside!

___ **2.** My best friend is nine and _____ years old.

___ **3.** The seats look _____ .

___ **4.** My folks have a _____ car.

___ **5.** I was so surprised I felt _____ .

a) well-worn

b) tongue-tied

c) one-half

d) blow-dry

e) ten-year-old

C **Use the words in the box to complete each open compound in the puzzle. Write the compound word on the line. Remember: The colored box stands for a space!**

chocolate   cream   bus   hold   fire   jay   look   one

Across:

4. _____

5. _____

6. _____

7. _____

8. _____

Down:

1. _____

2. _____

3. _____

Name _____

Writing Descriptive Passages

⭐ Adjectives are fine to use in descriptions, but sometimes they aren't as descriptive as they could be.

Rachel is such a nice person.

Use word pictures and interesting verbs to write better descriptions.

Rachel's warm smile seems to bring sunshine into any room.

Use words to show how and why things are the way they are.

Rachel always makes sure to greet new people. She tries to get to know them and help others to, as well.

A **Write a sentence that better describes the scene. Be creative!**

1. Derek was a good sport.

_____

2. The two were the best of friends.

_____

3. Jessi spends a lot of time outside.

_____

4. David really wanted to play soccer.

_____

5. Our neighbors are very neighborly.

_____

6. Alexis is great at playing games.

_____

★ When you write a descriptive paragraph, focus on one overall impression.

Confusing description: The beautiful woods felt creepy.

Are the woods beautiful or creepy? The two words don't seem to go together.

Better description: The dark woods close in around you and leave you feeling like you're being watched.

B **Write a descriptive passage. Use an idea from the box or one of your own.**

The Best Holiday Ever	Our Yard	My Mom
A Really Fun Day	Families Are Funny	An Interesting Movie
The Best Thing About Being the Oldest		
The Best Thing About Being the Youngest		

_____

_____

_____

_____

_____

_____

_____

_____

_____

_____

_____

47

JUST FOR FUN

Editing Your Work

 Editing your work is an important step in the writing process. Many tests ask you to show what you know about editing.

A **Eric wrote an essay about his mom's hobby. Help him revise and edit his report. Read the report and answer the questions that follow.**

Mom Autocrosses

1) My mom has an unusual hobby. 2) One Sunday each month, she races her car. 3) The kind of race she does is called autocross. 4) That means she takes her car around an obstacle course set up in a big empty parking lot. 5) They time how long she takes to get around the course. 6) They decide on the winners by comparing times of all the drivers. 7) She has three chances to "run" the course to get her best time.

1. Write the regular compound word from sentence 3.

_____

2. Write the two open compounds from sentence 4.

_____

3. Write the three adjectives from the paragraph.

_____

4. Write the prepositional phrase from sentence 3.

_____

5. Sentence 5 is a complex sentence. What is the dependent clause in sentence 5?

_____

6. Why isn't sentence 6 a complex sentence?

_____

7. Rewrite this phrase using better descriptive language: She takes her car around an obstacle course.

_____

Advantage Grammar Grade 4 © 2005 Creative Teaching Press

B **Continue editing and revising Eric's essay.**

1) The course the drivers run is different every time. 2) They set it up with big orange cones. 3) Each course will have several sharp turns and a slalom. 4) (A slalom is a zigzag shape.) 5) To learn the course, Mom walks the course with the other drivers. 6) I like to walk with her even though she won't let me talk. 7) "Shh, honey, I'm concentrating." she says. 8) Even though this kind of race is not very dangerous, we still want her to learn the course well. 9) If she misses just one turn, that run won't count!

10) Not many women do autocross. 11) So even if there are three women racing, Mom knows she'll get at least third place! 12) Dad comes and races his car, too. 13) But he is so proud of her, he'll brag about her times before he brags about his own!

1. What is the opposite adjective phrase from sentence 8?

_____

2. Rewrite sentence 7 correctly.

_____

_____

3. There is only one prepositional phrase in sentence 5. What is it?

_____

4. List the 14 adjectives. Remember: An adjective includes opposite phrases and numbers.

_____

_____

_____

5. There is only one complex sentence in the second paragraph. Which is it?

_____

6. Rewrite sentence 10 to show, rather than tell, a description.

_____

_____

_____

Name _____

Hannah wrote an essay about how she keeps in touch with family. Help her revise and edit her essay. Read the beginning of her essay and answer the questions that follow.

Long-Distance Cousins

1) When my cousin, Erin, told me she was moving from our town in Virginia to Kansas, I was so sad. 2) Erin is only one year older than I am, and we are best friends. 3) Besides, who would play Go Fish with me now?! 4) I felt sad and lonely. 5) And she wasn't even gone yet! 6) We tried to schedule lots of time playing in our swimming pool and skateboarding. 7) But she also had to help pack the moving van. 8) Then, one day she moved.

1. Which compound is not an open compound word?
   Ⓐ best friends
   Ⓑ swimming pool
   Ⓒ skateboarding
   Ⓓ moving van

2. Why is sentence 2 not a complex sentence?
   Ⓕ It is a sentence fragment.
   Ⓖ Both clauses are independent.
   Ⓗ Both clauses are dependent.
   Ⓙ It is not a sentence.

3. Which is the best descriptive way to write "I was so sad"?
   Ⓐ I felt so sad.
   Ⓑ I felt really bad.
   Ⓒ I was sad and blue.
   Ⓓ I felt sick to my stomach.

4. Which phrase is not a prepositional phrase?
   Ⓕ with me
   Ⓖ to schedule
   Ⓗ from our town
   Ⓙ in our swimming pool

Read the rest of Hannah's essay and answer the questions.

1) Once she had moved, however, we found that we could use the computer to spend time together. 2) Every other Friday, we "meet" online and play Go Fish. 3) We can IM (instant message) each other while we play. 4) In fact, we probably email each other almost every day. 5) Sometimes we discover that we're online at the same time, so we end up just using the keyboard to "talk" to each other. 6) Mom says, "You girls spend more time together now that you're apart."

5. Which word is not an adjective?
   Ⓐ instant
   Ⓑ every
   Ⓒ more
   Ⓓ time

6. Which sentence is a complex sentence?
   Ⓕ sentence 1
   Ⓖ sentence 2
   Ⓗ sentence 4
   Ⓙ sentence 5

7. Which is not a way to correctly rewrite sentence 6?
   Ⓐ "You girls spend more time together now that you're apart," Mom says,
   Ⓑ "You girls spend more time together now that you're apart," Mom says.
   Ⓒ Mom says, "You girls spend more time together now that you're apart."
   Ⓓ Mom says, "You girls spend more time together now that you're apart!"

8. Which phrase is a prepositional phrase?
   Ⓕ to spend
   Ⓖ meet online
   Ⓗ while we play
   Ⓙ at the same time

9. Which word is not a compound word?
   Ⓐ online
   Ⓑ IM
   Ⓒ email
   Ⓓ keyboard

Practice Test

Drew wrote an essay about a new hobby. Help him revise and edit his essay. Read the essay and answer the questions that follow.

Nordic Skiing

1) I just tried Nordic skiing with my family. 2) You may have heard it called cross-country skiing. 3) Nordic skiing can be done anywhere – mountains, hills, or flatland. 4) That's one thing that makes it different from downhill, or alpine, skiing. 5) No mountain needed, no lift needed, just strap on your skis and go! 6) If there's enough snow on the ground, we can ski right out our front door!

1. To make sentence 6 a declarative sentence, what end punctuation would you use?

   Ⓐ exclamation point   Ⓒ comma

   Ⓑ question mark   Ⓓ period

2. What could you do to sentence 2?

   Ⓕ Put it in parentheses.   Ⓗ Change the period to a question mark.

   Ⓖ Put it within quotation marks.   Ⓙ Underline the words *cross-country skiing*.

3. Which word is NOT a possessive pronoun?

   Ⓐ my   Ⓒ our

   Ⓑ we   Ⓓ your

4. What is true about the word *there's* in sentence 6?

   Ⓕ It is the contraction for "there is."   Ⓗ It shows possession.

   Ⓖ It is a compound word.   Ⓙ It is a plural noun.

5. What kind of word is *cross-country*?

   Ⓐ It is a plural noun.   Ⓒ It is a compound word.

   Ⓑ It is a superlative.   Ⓓ It is a possessive pronoun.

Read the rest of Drew's essay and answer the questions that follow.

1) If you have watched Nordic skiing at the Olympics, you have seen a style different from what we use. 2) Many skiers at competitions skate, instead of glide, over the snow. 3) Even their movements look like they're ice skating! 4) They use a slightly different ski also. 5) But both ways are very fast. 6) And when they come to a hill, all skiers go down the same way.

6. Which does NOT describe sentence 3?

Ⓕ fragment   Ⓗ supporting detail

Ⓖ exclamatory   Ⓙ complex sentence

7. What kind of paragraph is this?

Ⓐ compare and contrast   Ⓒ cause and effect

Ⓑ statement/example   Ⓓ none of the above

8. Which is NOT true about the word *they* in sentence 4?

Ⓕ *They* is a pronoun.   Ⓗ *They* is the object.

Ⓖ *They* is the subject.   Ⓙ *They* stands for "skiers at competitions."

9. Which phrase is a prepositional phrase?

Ⓐ you have watched   Ⓒ are very fast

Ⓑ a different ski   Ⓓ to a hill

10. Which is the topic sentence?

Ⓕ sentence 1   Ⓗ sentence 4

Ⓖ sentence 2   Ⓙ sentence 6

Practice Test

Jasmine wrote an essay about her pets. Help her revise and edit her essay. Read the essay and answer the questions that follow.

My Wild Ones

1) My family owns two special cats. 2) Tornado and Typhoon are Bengal cats. 3) The Bengal breed is related to a wild jungle cat. 4) With their spotted, lean bodies, they look a lot like jaguars. 5) Like jungle cats, they can jump unusually well. 6) And they love being high. 7) We always catch them on top of furniture – even the kitchen cupboards! 8) You might think that they are less friendly and more dangerous than other cats. 9) Actually, they are very sweet.

11. What kind of word is *Bengal* as it is used in the paragraph?

 Ⓐ prepositional phrase   Ⓒ adverb

 Ⓑ common noun   Ⓓ adjective

12. Which statement is NOT true about sentence 1?

 Ⓕ It is a simple sentence.   Ⓗ It is a supporting detail for the paragraph.

 Ⓖ It is in the present tense.   Ⓙ It contains both a subject and an object.

13. Which word is an adverb?

 Ⓐ wild   Ⓒ friendly

 Ⓑ unusually   Ⓓ sweet

14. What kind of sentence is sentence 7?

 Ⓕ declarative   Ⓗ imperative

 Ⓖ interrogative   Ⓙ exclamatory

15. Which sentence adds better descriptive details about sentence 9?

 Ⓐ They will even rub up against strangers.   Ⓒ They are very friendly.

 Ⓑ They're always cuddly.   Ⓓ They love to play.

Advantage Grammar Grade 4 © 2005 Creative Teaching Press

Name _____

Read the rest of Jasmine's essay and answer the questions that follow.

1) Another interesting thing about Bengals is their fur. 2) Bengal's fur is silkyer than most other cat's. 3) It also does not shed as much as most other furry pets. 4) In fact, Dad picked them out because of their fur. 5) "Good Kitty Magazine" said, "this special fur, called the glitter coat, is unique to the Bengal." 6) Most people who are allergic to cat fur are not allergic to these glitter coats! 7) It's a good thing, too, because Mom is allergic to cats (other cats, that is).

16. What kind of word is *these* in sentence 6?

   F adverb   H possessive pronoun

   G adjective   J demonstrative pronoun

17. How would you correct the word *silkyer* in sentence 2?

   A more silky   C most silky

   B silkier   D silkiest

18. Which past tense verb is regular?

   F was   H said

   G picked   J were

19. Which is not a way to write the magazine title correctly?

   A "Good Kitty Magazine"   C <u>Good Kitty Magazine</u>

   B *Good Kitty Magazine*   D none of the above

20. Which is the root word for the word *furry*?

   F furr   H fur

   G fure   J furey

21. Which word is NOT possessive?

   A their   C our

   B cat's   D it's

Answer Key

Lesson 1

A
1. Milky Way/galaxy
2. Earth/planet
3. sun/light/warmth
4. solar wind/sun
5. solar storms/Earth
6. sunspots/ sun
7. energy/sun
8. sunspots/Earth

B
Answers willl vary.

C
Common Nouns: stars, planets, solar wind, energy, sunspots, solar storms
Proper nouns: Milky Way, Earth, Sun, Venus, Mercury, Mars

D
1. are
2. circled
3. moves
4. see
5. zooms
6. is
7. burst
8. covered
9. look
10. were

Lesson 2

A
1. suddenly
2. near
3. soon
4. really
5. unexpectedly
6. down
7. slowly
8. much

B
Answers will vary.

C

```
A X Q H L P W D F S X B X
L Z U P T B C K A V W I N
Q C I D E M Y P R B H R O
L Z C N U E C R U D E L Y
M Z K S G F Q U N P B L E
N S L O W L Y N E X T Y T
Y U Y O T D A B A P X M M
C D K N L S C E R E Q Y C
H L X Z W A F J P K G A
B E K Y E X U O F T E N P
C N G A F T E R S K W B V
M L U C H T H E R E H L S
V Y Q C E U N P V I C T A
```

D
Where: there, far, near, next; When: often, soon, after, before; In What Way: quickly, slowly, suddenly, rudely

Lesson 3

A
1. ?
2. .
3. .
4. !
5. ?
6. .
7. .
8. ?
9. !
10. .

B
How does the sun affect the Earth? The sun gives Earth light and warmth. Energy from the sun causes weather and seasons. When the sun's rays hit the ground, they warm it. The warm ground heats the air above it. As the air heats, it rises and makes wind.

The sun also warms the water on Earth. Some of the warm water turns into a gas and rises into the air. When the gas cools off, it forms clouds. Sometimes the gases that make up clouds fall back to Earth as rain, snow, hail, or sleet. This is called the Water Cycle.

C
1. 178 Union St.
2. U.S.A.
3. 7:45 A.M.
4. Austin, Tex.
5. 47 Sunset Blvd.
6. Dr. Jones studies solar energy.
7. 8:50 P.M.
8. James Jones Sr.

Lesson 4

A
1. Earth is the third planet from the sun.
2. The sun pulls on the planets with a force called gravity.
3. Green plants soak up the sun's energy and turn it into food.
4. Sunspots look like dark.
5. Energy from the sun causes weather and seasons

B
1. The nine planets orbit the sun, | and Earth is one of these nine planets.
3. Solar storms often hit Earth, | but we cannot always see or feel them
8. The gas cools off, | and then it forms clouds.

C
Answers will vary.

Lesson 5

A
The sun is a star. It is a huge ball of glowing gases. The sun is one of at least 200 billion stars in the Milky Way galaxy. The Milky Way is the galaxy we live in.

The sun is a medium-sized star, but it is much larger than Earth. The sun is 865,000 miles (1,392,000 km) across. That makes it more than 100 times wider than Earth.

Advantage Grammar Grade 4 © 2005 Creative Teaching Press

B

The sun gives energy for living things to grow. Green plants soak up the sun's energy and turn it into food. When plant-eating animals eat the plants, they receive this energy. When meat-eating animals eat the plant-eating animals, the energy is passed on again. The sun is very important to Earth as a living planet.

C

Answers will vary.

Lesson 6

A

knows/nose, son/sun, weather/whether, winds/wins, hour/our

pail/pale, weight/wait, fair/fare, knot/not, ate/eight, no/know, Sunday/sundae, hear/here, be/bee, pair/pear blew/blue, some/sum, rays/raise, see/sea, flew/flu

B

Answers will vary.

C

to, too, two; fore, four, for; they're, their, there; sow, so, sew; by, buy, bye; dear, deer; bare, bear; capitol, capital; scene, seen; one, won; allowed, aloud; clause, claws; groan, grown; reed, read; rose, rows; steal, steel; tail, tale; weak, week; hare, hair; bawl, ball; hey, hay; it's, its; knight, night; cell, sell; lead, led; knew, new; nose, knows; creek, creak; mail, male; pear, pair; pour, poor; meat, meet; knead, need; pause, paws; plain, plane

D

1. rose/rows
2. it's/its
3. whether/weather
4. son/sun
5. to/too
6. eight/ate
7. our/hour
8. blew/blue

Lesson 7

A

1. The sun affects Earth in many ways.
2. sun, Earth, light, warmth
3. use, grow
4. Green plants soak up the sun's energy, I and they turn it into food.
5. Sentence 7: Without the sun, Earth would not have any life at all.

B

1. whether/weather
2. sun (proper), water (common), Earth (proper)
3. quickly
4. When this warm air meets cold air, it makes wind.
5. The gas cools off, then it forms clouds.

Lesson 8

1. B
2. J
3. A
4. H
5. A
6. J
7. B
8. F

Unit 2
Lesson 9

A

1. I
2. R
3. I
4. R

B

1. found
2. named
3. wrote
4. became

C

Regular Verbs: learned, decided, studied, stayed, dreamed, guessed, moved, liked
Irregular Verbs: rose, gave, knew, spoke, forgot, saw, fought, grew

D

Regular Verbs: loved, tried, learned, asked
Irregular Verbs: sent, bought, won, took

Lesson 10

A

Present Tense	Past Tense	Future Tense
rise	rose	will rise
give	gave	will give
learn	learned	will learn
know	knew	will know
stay	stayed	will stay
decide	decided	will decide
speak	spoke	will speak
forget	forgot	will forget
see	saw	will see
study	studied	will study
dream	dreamed	will dream
guess	guessed	will guess
move	moved	will move
like	liked	will like
send	sent	will send
find	found	will find
feel	felt	will feel
ask	asked	will ask
become	became	will become

B

1. dreamed
2. spoke
3. asked
4. declared
5. hoped
6. helped
7. finished
8. joined

C

Answers will vary.

Lesson 11

A

1. America's
2. nation's
3. Edison's

B

Answers will vary.

Answer Key

C

Words	Contraction
she will	she'll
will not	won't
she would	she'd
do not	don't
I will	I'll
you will	you'll
I am	I'm
he will	he'll
I would	I'd
they will	they'll
cannot	can't
was not	wasn't
you will	you'll
were not	weren't

D

1. didn't
2. wasn't
3. don't
4. I'm

Lesson 12

A

1. Dr. Martin Luther King spoke to Americans about civil rights.
2. Rosa Parks boycotted the public bus service in Montgomery, Alabama.
3. Benjamin Franklin invented the lightning rod.
4. Roger Williams founded the state of Rhode Island.
5. Dwight D. Eisenhower was the 34th president of the United States.
6. Carrie Chapman Catt lead the National American Woman Suffrage Association.

B

Answers will vary.

C

1. named
2. James Madison
3. called
4. Dr. Martin Luther King, Jr.
5. received
6. became

D

1. Benjamin Franklin was a man of many talents who invented bifocal glasses and the lightning rod. He also was among those who signed the Declaration of Independence, which he also helped to write.
2. Dwight D. Eisenhower, after World War II, was elected the 34th president of the United States. He was also, during World War II, the Supreme Commander of U.S. troops in Europe.

Lesson 13

A

1. CE
2. CC
3. TS

B

1. because
2. although
3. first
4. as a result
5. finally
6. for example

C

Cause and Effect	Statement and Example	Time Sequence	Compare and Contrast
because as a result	for example	first finally	although

Lesson 14

A

Contraction	Spelled Out Words
I'll	I will
she'll	she will
he'll	he will
they'll	they will
you'll	you will
aren't	are not
won't	will not
can't	cannot
wasn't	was not
weren't	were not
don't	do not
I'd	I would
she'd	she would
he'd	he would
we'd	we would
they'd	they would
I'm	I am
you're	you are
who's	who is
doesn't	does not

B

Answers will vary.

C

did not, wasn't, could not, did not, he would

D

Colin's family wasn't wealthy. His father, Luther, worked in the stockroom. He'd come home tired every evening. His mother, Maud, felt she wasn't making enough money for the family to survive.

Lesson 15

A

1. He was born a Quaker's son.
2. started—past tense
3. unsuccessful
4. After a short education, he started to work. At first he worked for his father. Later he worked as an officer of the excise, which is a sort of tax collector. During this time, Thomas Paine was an unsuccessful man. He was twice fired, or let go, from his post.
5. landed

B

1. he'd—he had
2. He thought the Colonies should not stay dependent on England. They should become a new nation.
3. But Paine disagreed even more.

Advantage Grammar Grade 4 © 2005 Creative Teaching Press

4. So, on January 10, 1776, Paine's ideas on American independence were spelled out in his pamphlet "Common Sense."

Lesson 16

A

1. B	5. D
2. J	6. F
3. A	7. B
4. H	8. H

Unit 3

Lesson 17

A

1. denser	4. roomier
2. smaller	5. more able
3. more colorful	

B

1. redder	4. more stable
2. lighter	5. tinier
3. harder	6. richer

C

more large – larger, heavyer – heavier, biger – bigger, gooder – better, more long – longer, littler – less, buoyanter – more buoyant, gooder – better

Lesson 18

A

1. hardest	4. smokiest
2. softest	5. most expensive
3. most yellow	

B

1. frostiest	4. most delicate
2. sharpest	5. most useful
3. heaviest	6. wettest

C

Answers may vary.

1. best	4. least
2. oldest	5. greatest
3. worst	

D

Answers may vary.

Lesson 19

A

1. NMI	4. NMI
2. FE	5. NMI
3. FE	

B

1. Water (the most common liquid) can be used in experiments.
2. You can do many things to liquids (as long as you don't break the container).
3. You can change the temperature of a liquid (by boiling or freezing it).
4. Take an experiment out of the light (or the sunshine) to see what it does.

5. Mix something into the liquid to see how it reacts (changes).
6. Or just observe (watch) what happens to the liquid over time.
7. You may need to check your experiment every day (or even every hour).

C

1. Magic tricks are usually done by 1) distraction of the audience, 2) fancy gadgets, 3) science, or 4) lightning-quick movements.
2. My favorite book explains magic (*Sh! Don't Tell* by R. Deisch).
3. I like magic because (a) it is entertaining and (b) I like trying to figure out the trick.
4. I want to do magic because A) I like to perform, B) I enjoy magic, and C) I want the fun gadgets!
5. I need to practice a trick called Find the Bunny (*Tricky Tricks*, p. 68).
6. Try this magic trick at home (it's actually science).

7. Collect the following items: 1) pitcher of water, 2) a penny, and 3) a clear glass.
8. Place the penny under the empty glass (on a flat surface).
9. Look through the side (not the top) of the glass.
10. Pour water slowly into the glass until the penny disappears (look through the top to see that the penny is still there).
11. The experiment is called the Disappearing Penny Trick (*Bending Light*, p. 174).
12. To learn more why this trick works, read *Science Through Magic* (chapter 8).
13. Light moves through air differently than it moves through water (such as in the ocean).
14. Water refracts (or bends) the light.

Lesson 20

A

1. In	6. Im
2. D	7. In
3. E	8. Im
4. Im	9. In
5. D	10. E

B

Sentences may vary.

1. Do the experiment in part A with both juice and bottled water.
2. What would happen if you continue to boil the water?
3. You should be careful because the hot stove can be dangerous.
4. The results surprised me!

C

Sentences may vary.

Lesson 21

A

1. TS	4. SD
2. SD	5. SD
3. SD	6. SD

Answer Key

B
1. TS
2. SD
3. SD
4. SD
5. SD
6. SD

C
1. So there are several ways to change the state of matter.
2. If you have, you already know that when a liquid changes to a solid, it gets bigger!

Lesson 22
A
1. buses
2. sticks
3. armies
4. matches
5. plates

B
1. kinds
2. objects
3. energies
4. metals
5. wires
6. switches
7. mixes
8. clouds

C
1. women
2. children
3. buses
4. stories
5. deer
6. car
7. couches
8. paths

D

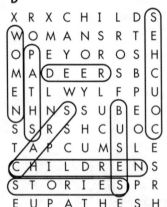

Lesson 23
A
1. 2, 3, 4
2. 5
3. 3
4. Declarative: 1, 2, 3, or 5
   Interrogative: 7
   Imperative: 8
   Exclamatory: 4 or 6
5. energies, cements
6. best
7. Insulators can do both things – but some are better than others!

8. sample sentence #2: Can heat or electricity be stopped this way?

B
1. The ending parenthesis should be inside the end punctuation.
2. plugs
3. 1
4. 8
5. 2
6. Plastic seems to be the most common insulator for wires.
7. longer or shorter
8. longest or shortest
9. plastics, glasses
10. But can electricity be dangerous to people?

Lesson 24
1. B
2. H
3. C
4. J
5. D
6. F
7. A
8. H
9. B

Unit 4
Lesson 25
A
SP stands for subject pronouns, OP stands for object pronouns
1. SP – He, OP – them
2. SP – It, OP – me
3. SP – He, OP – them
4. SP – She, OP – us

B
1. It stretches across five time zones.
2. They make up about 4% of the population of Canada.
3. She plans to take a trip to the French-speaking province of Quebec.

C
1. Mrs. Marco took us on a trip to the Grand Canyon.
2. We sold them to earn money for the trip.
3. The class washed them to earn money.

D
Sentences will vary.

Lesson 26
A
1. in
2. of
3. with
4. under

B
1. from – Spain, in – 1821
2. for – tourists
3. for – fields
4. through – city, in – Costa Rica
5. in – country
6. of – population, in – heartland
7. of – Chile, with – winters and summers
8. before – Easter

Advantage Grammar Grade 4 © 2005 Creative Teaching Press

9. to – pyramids
10. in – Guatemala, in – spring

C
1. of the population, in Santiago, Chile
2. on the Caribbean, on the Pacific
3. of Columbia, of rain
4. in the Atlantic northeast, in November
5. in Monument Valley, from red sandstone
6. over the world, after famous explorers

Lesson 27
A
1. The interior lowlands around Hudson's Bay make up 80% of Canada's land area.
2. The St. Lawrence River and Great Lakes lowlands are the most populated areas of Canada.
3. Many Asians have moved to Canada in recent years.
4. Kim Campbell was Canada's first woman premier.
5. The Northwest Territories cover 1.3 million square miles, or one-third of the country.

B
1. D
2. G
3. C
4. F
5. C
6. G

Lesson 28
A   Sample answers below:
1. There were many ways settlers traveled across the country, such as on foot, by horse, by wagon, and by boat.
2. Rivers are a very valuable resource because they provide transportation and water for irrigation.
3. The plantations of the South greatly prospered because of cotton and tobacco growing.
4. The remaining rainforests are slowly being cut down by farmers and loggers.
5. The Rocky Mountains in the western United States have many minerals including gold, silver, and copper.
6. Between 1860 and 1910, 23 million immigrants crossed the Atlantic and Pacific Oceans to seek opportunity in America.
7. Progress is being made to protect the environment by creating national parks and wildlife preserves.
8. The geography of California attracts many filmmakers due to its sunny, dry climate and access to beaches, mountains, and deserts.
9. During the 1920s, many African Americans moved to the North to seek better jobs and less discrimination.
10. The United States has a full range of climate conditions including floods, tornadoes, hurricanes, thunderstorms, and droughts.

Lesson 29
A
1. knack
2. knap
3. quartz
4. quantity
5. knew
6. qualified
7. knoll
8. question

B
1. quite
2. known
3. knights
4. quarry

C
1. quarrel
2. quite
3. quiet
4. knack
5. quarters
6. known
7. quart
8. knapsack

Lesson 30
A
Underline the first sentence and circle the rest of the paragraph.

B
Paragraphs will vary.

C
Paragraphs will vary.

D
Paragraphs will vary.

Lesson 31
A
1. Mexico, because it is a proper noun.
2. he, the farmer
3. subject pronoun
4. of –hole, for – place
5. in a knoll, on the farm
6. Sentences will vary. Sample sentence 4 given: But the sky was clear of any clouds!
7. earthquakes, quakes, quickly
8. knew, knoll

B
1. Because the first word in the sentence needs to be capitalized as well as proper names.
2. Sentences will vary. Sample sentence given: In a short time, the volcano continued to grow over the field.
3. from lightning, by the volcano
4. on – forests, for – years, since – time
5. quite - quiet
6. know - known
7. it - ash
8. details

Lesson 32
1. C
2. J
3. A
4. H
5. C
6. J
7. B
8. F

Unit 5
Lesson 33
A
1. their
2. your
3. mine
4. My
5. its

B
1. c
2. e
3. b
4. d
5. g

Answer Key

C

1. her
2. hers
3. Her
4. their
5. his or their
6. your
7. mine
8. his
9. his
10. ours
11. its
12. my

D

Sentences will vary.

Lesson 34

A

1. those
2. this
3. those
4. That
5. this
6. those
7. These
8. Such
9. that
10. these
11. Such
12. this

B

Sample answers below:
1. a hobby
2. comfortable clothes or shoes
3. description of what babies do
4. a heavy box
5. a type of food

C

1. a. these
2. b. such
3. b. This
4. a. That
5. a. those

D

Sentences will vary.

Lesson 35

A

1. a
2. a
3. b
4. b
5. a
6. b
7. b
8. b

B

Sample sentences below:
1. My favorite author is Jerry Spinelli because his characters are one-of-a-kind.
2. The writer Jerry Spinelli usually writes about convincing settings, realistic situations, and believable people.
3. I like books that had surprise endings and also funny scenes.
4. I like writing the ending of stories, but I don't like writing the beginnings.
5. Many writers started writing poems and ended up writing songs.

C

Sample sentences below:
1. After school, I will go to the library, pick out a book, and start it.

Lesson 36

A

1. Try to solve the mysteries when reading Encyclopedia Brown Solves Them All.
2. One chapter that is hard to solve is "The Case of the Hair Driers."
3. The Wright brothers named their plane The Flyer.
4. Read about the history of the plane in Aircrafters Magazine.
5. "The Very First Plane" is the title of the article.
6. People read the forecast in our newspaper, The Westlife Journal.
7. We sang the song "You Are My Sunshine" together.
8. In the movie Shrek, they redid the song "I'm a Believer."
9. The funniest section in the magazine Reader's Digest is called "All in a Day's Work."
10. The first chapter in the book Stuart Little is "In the Drain."

B

Answers will vary.

C

Answers will vary

Lesson 37

A

1. sitting
2. biter
3. having
4. fibber
5. funny
6. giver
7. dragging
8. swimmer
9. taming
10. raced

B

1. bat
2. write
3. big
4. run
5. care
6. shine
7. dim
8. bake
9. tan
10. rake

C

1. g
2. f
3. c
4. b
5. d
6. e
7. a
8. h

Lesson 38

A

1. Although they are not the same, the movie Iron Will and the book Stone Fox are very similar.
2. Answers may vary. Sample answers given:
   Similarities: the hero's name is Will, dogsled race, money needed for farm, a dog is a main character, both named after a character
   Differences: dog's name (Gus or Searchlight), money needed for different reasons (grandfather needs it or mom needs it and he's going to college), the ending is different (dog dies or lives), named after different characters

Advantage Grammar Grade 4 © 2005 Creative Teaching Press

3. Sample answers below:
    similarities: same, similar, and, both
    differences: though, but, however, differences, different
    other words: alike, differ, yet, not

B

Answers will vary.

Lesson 39
A
1. Underline the titles of the books (4 times)
2. 2, These, stands for the two books
3. 2 – my, 3 – his, 8 – Their
4. Besides having parts that aren't realistic, both books also have parts that do seem real.
5. having - have

B
1. Underline the titles of the books (8 times) and add quotes to sentence 5 as follows: was "The Three Erics."
2. 4 – These – stands for the thirty short stories, 10 – That – serious tone with funny parts
3. it's should be its
4. I am glad I don't have to choose and I can enjoy both stories! or I am glad that I don't have to choose and that I can enjoy both stories!
5. 5 – My, 9 – its
6. funny – fun
7. Similarities: both written by Louis Sachar, both are funny and have crazy stories, some parts seemed real and others didn't, weird names in both (including back wards names)
    Differences: *Holes* is more realistic and serious, it was one story and had one main character while *Sideways Stories* was many stories with a different main character in each, *Holes* took place in three different times

Lesson 40
1. C	6. H
2. J	7. B
3. B	8. F
4. H	9. D
5. B	

Unit 6
Lesson 41
A
1. delicious	7. steady, even
2. old log	8. old and worn
3. some pink	9. tired, sore, and happy
4. little, white	10. cheerful young Asian
5. long, rolling, and fast	11. crustless ham
6. peaceful	12. big, white cowboy

B
Sentences will vary. Sample use of adjectives below:
1. uninterested or less interested
2. unsurprised or less surprised
3. least lonely
4. unlike or dislike

C
Sentences will vary.

Lesson 42
A
1. from the floor
2. to another player
3. down the court
4. in front, of the basketball hoop
5. of the greatest importance
6. back to him
7. until the best moment
8. around an opponent
9. through the hoop
10. according to his fans
11. without his teammates
12. throughout the season

B
1. through the crack
3. because of his kind words
7. at noon
8. at the park
10. instead of milk

C
Answers will vary.

Lesson 43
A
2. subjects: I, I; predicates: could reach, started taking
4. subjects: I, it; predicates: thought, would be
7. subjects: I, my music; predicates: stuck, improved
8. subjects: I, I; predicates: wonder, keep learning
10. subjects: he, that; predicates: sang, made
11. subjects: it, it; predicates: can be, is

B
Sample sentences below:
Before she was my age, my sister wanted to learn.
She often acted like she was a karate black belt.
When she started classes, she was only a white belt.
My sister worked hard so that she could become a brown belt.
Someday she'll be a black belt if she sticks with it.

C
Sentences will vary.

Lesson 44
A
1. Jon said, "What has 18 legs and catches flies?"
    "That sounds like a baseball team," said Megan.
2. "What do you do when 19 guys are running at you?" asked Megan. "Run faster?" said Jon. Megan said, "No, you throw the football!"

Answer Key

3. "Why was Cinderella thrown off the basketball team?" asked Jon. Megan said, "Because her glass slippers kept breaking?" "Because she ran away from the ball," said Jon.
4. "Why did the golfer bring an extra pair of pants?" asked Megan. Jon said, "You got me there – why?" "In case he got a hole in one," said Megan.

B
1. "Why didn't the nose make the volleyball team?" asked Jon. "I don't know," said Megan. Jon said, "Because it didn't get picked."

C
Megan asked, "Why did the coach go to the bank?" "Perhaps he wanted to get his quarterback," said Jon.
2. "Why can't you take a chicken to go fishing?" asked Megan. "Because the clucking will scare the fish away," said Jon. "Well, yes, and the chicken will eat all the bait," said Megan.

D
Sentences will vary.

Lesson 45
A
Sample words are: notebook, inbox, butterfly, caveman, somewhere, someday, everywhere, nowhere, midday, midnight, daybreak, breakfast, sleepover, flyover

B
1. d
2. c
3. a
4. e
5. b

C
Across: 4. chocolate chip
5. hold up
6. look out
7. blue jay
8. no one
Down: 1. ice cream
2. school bus
3. fire engine

Lesson 46
A
Sentences will vary.

B
Paragraphs will vary.

Lesson 47
A
1. autocross
2. obstacle course, parking lot
3. big, empty, best
4. of race
5. how long she takes to get around the course
6. It has two predicates, but only one subject
7. Sentences will vary.

B
1. not very dangerous
2. "Shh, honey, I'm concentrating," she says. OR She says, "Shh, honey, I'm concentrating."
3. with the other drivers
4. different, every, big, orange, several, sharp, zigzag, other, dangerous, one, not many, three, third, proud
5. 11
6. Sentences will vary.

Lesson 48
1. C
2. G
3. C
4. G
5. D
6. F
7. A
8. J
9. B

Practice Test
1. D
2. F
3. B
4. F
5. C
6. F
7. A
8. H
9. D
10. F
11. D
12. H
13. B
14. J
15. A
16. J
17. B
18. G
19. A
20. H
21. D

Advantage Grammar Grade 4 © 2005 Creative Teaching Press